MASTERS OF THE SCALPEL

The Story of Surgery

MASTERS OF
THE SCALPEL

THE STORY OF SURGERY
Illustrated with 60 photographs

by Sarah R. Riedman

RAND McNALLY & COMPANY

CHICAGO   NEW YORK   SAN FRANCISCO

617.09

CONTENTS

26018

ILLUSTRATIONS

CHAPTER ONE

Mending a Human Heart

It is 10 P.M. on the night of May 6, 1958, and television viewers who have tuned in are witnessing the start of a unique dramatic production. There are no billboards, no lobby, no box office, no stage props, and the theater is really "off Broadway," for the stage is set in an operating room of University Hospital in New York City. The characters are well rehearsed for their parts in a true story — a living drama that will answer the question:

WILL THREE-YEAR-OLD MABEL CHIN WAKE UP WITH A NORMAL HEART — MENDED BY THE SKILLED HANDS OF A HEART SURGEON?

Two-and-a-half million people within reach of the TV waves watch and wait in suspense for the plot to unfold . . . .

ACT I

Scene: Operating Amphitheatre

Beneath several layers of sterile sheets the anesthetized patient is asleep, free of pain, and unaware of her leading role in the unprecedented spectacular. Hovering around the operating table is the white-gowned surgical team, each member in position for his or her assigned task. Their eyes are on the operating field — a four-inch-square opening in the child's chest, revealed by the folded-back sheets. Between two of her ribs, spread apart by metal retractors, the heart is seen to pulse in regular rhythm, with each beat pumping its life's blood through every organ of the little body.

Watching steadily over Mabel's covered head is an important member of the team, the anesthetist. It is his job to provide the patient with just the right amount of anesthesia and oxygen to keep her unconscious, relaxed, and alive. In this operation — with the chest open — he is especially busy, for he has had to take over the work of Mabel's breathing muscles. Because their motion would interfere with the operation, these muscles have been temporarily immobilized. Besides, with the chest open, the lungs collapse. The anesthetist must keep them artificially inflated.

His assistant is far from idle. As a member of the team he controls several machines: one to record the blood pressure, one the beat of the heart, and another to keep track of its electrical impulses. These machines tell him whether or not the patient needs medicine or additional fluid, and he is responsible for seeing that the lungs are sufficiently inflated and the tissues flushed with an adequate supply of blood.

The "scrub nurse" (the one who scrubs her hands clean of germs in the same way as the surgeon and his assistant do) hands the surgeon the right instrument for each step: the hemostat for pinching off an oozing blood vessel, forceps to remove pads of fat, a probe to separate the delicate membranes and clear the field. At the right moment a sponge and suction tube are required to keep the field clear and dry. A syringe keeps the tissues moistened with saline solution. The

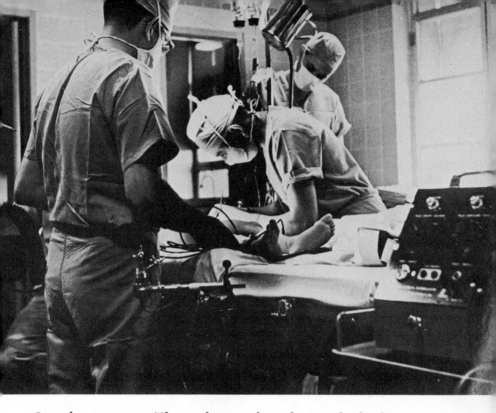

Open-heart surgery. The machine at the right records the electrical impulses from the heart. This is one way the surgeon has of knowing how the patient is doing during the operation

scrub nurse's assistant keeps the instrument tray filled, and the circulating nurse replenishes the supply of gauze, swabs, sponges, syringes.

The assistant surgeon, never taking his eyes from the operating field, is opposite the surgeon, ready for any emergency, and little is said, for this operation has been "rehearsed" many times. His movements coordinate with those of the surgeon's in the perfect timing of practiced teammates.

The leader of the team is now ready to perform the major part of the operation: correction of what he has diagnosed as a fault in the patient's circulation.

Mabel Chin was born with a defect called a *patent ductus arteriosus*. The *ductus arteriosus* — a tiny vessel about the size of a medicine dropper — connects the two main arteries leading from the heart — the aorta and the pulmonary artery. Normally this vessel closes at birth; in Mabel's heart it had remained open or "patent."

This flaw in the body's plumbing nearly always means a shortened and crippled life. When it is open, the little duct shunts some of the blood from the aorta, the main pipeline that feeds all parts of the body, into the pulmonary artery, which carries blood to the lungs. With each beat the heart pumps harder to make up for the loss of the shunted blood. After a while the heart becomes enlarged, the pulmonary artery stretches with its additional burden, and the open duct often becomes infected.

It all spells out the life of a cardiac cripple: shortness of breath from running or skipping rope; later on, from merely walking across the street; and, if the duct is extra-large, failure even to grow. Mabel is lucky to be a child of our time, for had she been born just a few decades ago, thirty-five handicapped years would have been her most optimistic life expectancy.

ACT II

The camera now focuses on the surgeon. If he is successful, he will mend Mabel's heart and restore her to a normal life.

However, as he begins the operation, he is not completely satisfied that his diagnosis is correct. All the tests have indicated a patent duct, but he will not be absolutely sure until he has cut through the many pads of fat and fibrous tissue and exposed the little channel.

With infinite patience, he cuts away each thread of overlying tissue in the tiny trouble spot. Without haste, yet not wasting a moment, he deftly manipulates the delicate instruments to spread and peel away bits of tissue. The greatest care is demanded, for the slightest slip could mean a cut blood vessel or a torn nerve. From years of study he knows the anatomy of the part and where to look for the danger points. Here he recognizes the large nerve that slows the heartbeat, the smaller branch of which controls the muscles of the larynx. If this is damaged it may mean loss of speech. The hazards are many and require exact knowledge and great skill.

His team on its toes — mopping, flushing, lifting, clearing. Now and then the anesthetist interrupts the main procedure by a little extra inflation of the lung which overlaps the working field, but the surgeon doesn't lose any time. With the tip of his forefinger he feels for the pulsation in the duct. What he can't see he must feel. But not all the tissue has been removed yet, and he continues the work with a probe.

Finally he reaches the duct and, with his fingertips, feels the wall pulsate. His diagnosis was correct. The *ductus arteriosus* is patent!

Lifting up the little vessel, he places a ligature under it, ties the ends of the thread, and repeats the procedure with a second ligature at a little distance from the first. The assistant hands him another and then a fourth. One has to be sure. Or as the surgeons say: "Two for the patient, one for the surgeon, and one for God."

The assistant anesthetist reports on the blood pressure: "The diastolic is 70." This means that the "lower" blood pressure (during the heart's resting interval) has gone up.

The "leak" has been fixed! The shunt has been blocked.

The surgeon has performed this operation many times,

but his sense of release is profound, as it always is with each successful repetition. The hazards have been overcome, and the patient has been saved for a normal life.

ACT III

The wind-up, and perhaps to some an anti-climax, but what remains to be done is no less important. The retractors must be removed and the lips of the incision allowed to approach each other. The last part dissected is the first part to be sewn up. The surgeon and his assistant work as smoothly as one man with four hands. Gently, one layer after another, they pull the spread tissues together at the cut, stitching and tying, stitching and tying. Between stitches, the open area is covered with moistened gauze to protect the tissues from damage by drying and exposure.

Finally, only the skin remains open at the cut. Point by point the two sides are carefully matched, for a good surgeon always leaves as small a scar as conditions allow.

As the incision is being closed, the anesthetist reduces the amount of anesthetic. He watches the surgeon, and times his own operations so that the patient will awaken at almost the same time as the last stitch is made. Now the drug that temporarily paralyzed Mabel's breathing muscles is wearing off and she begins to breathe naturally.

The sheets are removed, the patient's face is uncovered, the machines are detached, the instruments are picked up for scrubbing. The surgeon leaves the amphitheatre and removes his gloves, gown, cap, and face mask.

"Wake up, open your eyes," the nurse says gently, and as the screen darkens Mabel is wheeled into the recovery room.

Thirty years ago Mabel's operation would have been impossible. "One organ on which you cannot operate is the heart," medical students were taught. Today, the surgeon will tell you, this type of surgery, in the hands of a specialist who has made a careful study of the heart, is as simple and safe as removing an appendix. In about 30 hospitals in New York City alone, some 150 surgeons regularly perform similar miracles.

Less than a century ago no operations were possible without an enormously high risk of death from infection. A century-and-a-quarter ago they could not be done without agonizing pain. Until these and other drawbacks were overcome, surgery advanced at the pace of an inch-worm. Then came the great breakthroughs: the discovery of anesthetics; the discovery of the cause of infection and how to prevent and combat it; the development of the knowledge of how to control hemorrhage and shock. With these, surgery strode forward in seven-league boots.

Our story tells of the earlier trials, failures, fumblings, and desperation, and of the giant achievements of the last hundred years, the century of surgery. It is the story of a series of battles in man's continued war against disease and the effects of violent injury. Its heroes, masters of the scalpel, are the men of courage and vision who fought stubbornly against the ignorant, the timid, and the blind until the paths they blazed became safe highroads for others to follow.

Note: The New York Heart Association sponsored the televising of the Mabel Chin heart operation for two reasons: to show that the possibility of repairing certain heart conditions was an everyday fact; and to dramatize the comparative safety of heart surgery which the average individual, at that time, thought to be extremely dangerous. The program was co-produced by the New York Heart Association and television channel 5, New York City. Dr. Jere W. Lord, Jr., who was President of the New York Heart Association at the time, performed the televised operation.

CHAPTER TWO

Surgery in Ancient Times

For almost as long as people have known sickness, they have tried to heal with the knife. How far back must we unwind the clock of history to find the first operation? Holes gouged out in skulls unearthed among the remains of primitive people tell part of the story.

The amphitheatre might have been a cave, the instrument a stone flint, and the patient the victim of a club wound on the head, a sufferer of unbearable headaches, or demented and thought to be possessed of a demon. That some survived such brutal "cures" is astonishing. The growth of new bone around the edges of the hole is evidence that the patient somehow came through the ordeal alive. For only living tissue can grow.

History records that surgery was practiced by the Babylonians in the ancient kingdom of Mesopotamia over 4,000 years ago. Among the relics of this ancient empire are not only remnants of the Hanging Gardens, but also the Code of Hammurabi, which included a set of rules for the regulation of both surgical practices and the surgeon's fees. A successful operation performed on a rich man was worth five times the fee for a similar operation on his slave. If the patient died, the hapless surgeon lost more than his fee: his right hand was cut off, a sure way of preventing any more such fatalities under his knife.

Similar laws were also set down in ancient Persia, where a surgeon was allowed to practice only after he had performed three successful operations on infidels. (In these ancient civilizations the physicians were priests, and one of their functions was to placate the gods; this law was intended to give special protection to the believer.)

Egypt has sometimes been called the "cradle of medicine," probably because the record is more complete even than it is for China and India, older than Egypt, where highly developed civilizations also flourished. This record is available because in Egypt not all of the doctors were priests. Most were scribes, men of learning who could wield a pen as well as a surgical knife. They received their medical training in schools connected with the courts, chancelleries, and temples, and were able to describe the art of healing in a series of books called the "papyri." These included surgical procedures practiced from 1900 to 1350 B. C.

Medical drawings, tools, and instruments found with mummies and other human remains in excavated burial crypts and temples are additional proof that Egyptian surgery had reached a relatively advanced stage. Fractures were set, abscesses drained, cataracts extracted, surface tumors removed, abdominal and other wounds closed with tape, and jaw bones drilled for abscesses in tooth sockets.

Strangely enough, doctors had become highly specialized even in those days. In the tomb of the Chief of the Court Physicians discovered at Gizeh were buried the "palace eye physician," "palace dentist," and "physician of the belly."

Surgery in Ancient Egypt

One papyrus, dating from the seventeenth century B. C., deals only with surgery after violent accidents.

The surgical section of the Ebers papyrus (about the fourteenth century B. C.) speaks of fractures and dislocations, tells how to treat carbuncles, tuberculous glands, hernias, and varicose (swollen and blocked) veins. It also warns the surgeon on bulging arteries: "Thou shalt not put thy hand," a strict caution against an always dangerous operation. There are many other words of genuine surgical wisdom in this famous papyrus. When removing a cyst (a sac containing fluid or solid tissue), the surgeon is warned to be sure to leave nothing of the wall, or the cyst will grow again. To cope with loss of blood — one of the many serious risks in surgery — he is told to apply hot instruments to the open wound: the heat seals the ends of opened blood vessels. This method, called cautery or cauterization, was an accepted surgical technique especially for large wounds, like those occurring after amputations, until the last century. It is dramatically described in *Moby Dick*.

From other papyri we learn that the Egyptians used metal instruments of varied shapes and sizes, absorbent lint for sponging up blood, plugs to stop nosebleed, linen bandages (manufactured by embalmers), adhesive plaster made of strips of the same linen for holding together "the two lips of a gaping wound." The Egyptians had sutures for stitching, several kinds of wooden splints for immobilizing fractured limbs, and other splints — padded with soft linen — to support

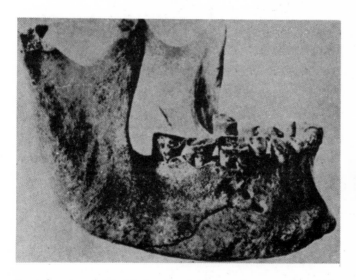

Jaw showing drilled holes for draining abscesses (Egypt)

(Left): Ancient surgical instruments used in Egypt (Cairo Museum); (Above): Description of cancer of the breast, from Ed. Smith Papyrus, Egypt, 3000 B.C.: "If thou examinest a man having bulging tumors on his breast . . . large spreading and hard touching like green fruit . . . an ailment with which I will contend. There is no treatment."

a broken nose or to keep the mouth open to permit feeding.

In ancient Greece, medical practice consisted mainly of miracle cures performed by the priests in the temples where the gods worshiped. The priests were spiritual descendants of Aesculapius, god of medicine, and were supposed to have inherited the secrets of his healing art.

Nevertheless, it was in Greece, beginning with the sixth century B. C., that the earliest attempts at the scientific study of nature were made. Scholars began to study the world around them, and man was studied as part of nature. The first Greek physicians were philosophers who interested themselves in medical problems, among other things. What made people sick, they asked, and how could people be guarded against illness, and how could they be cured? Medical schools arose in Croton, Sicily, Rhodes, and on the island of Cos.

The men who wrote the Egyptian papyri remain unknown. But around 460 B. C., on the island of Cos, a future doctor was born — Hippocrates. To this day his name is universally known, as a symbol of the great, good, and wise medical doctor. The Hippocratic writings, a collection of textbooks, speeches, notes, and extracts attributed to the master, may well have been the work of many doctors. In any case, these works were to influence medical thought and practice for centuries.

Although few factual details can be found about the life of Hippocrates, we know that he was famed as a practitioner and teacher of the art of healing. True, he was a member of the guild of Askelapiads, supposedly founded by Aesculapius. Actually he and other guild physicians had broken away from religious cures. Their approach, based on the treatment of physical symptoms, was the beginning of the scientific approach to healing.

It is related that Hippocrates was taught first by his father, and then by the famous doctor, Herodicus. When he had completed his apprenticeship, he embarked on a career of travel throughout Greece, everywhere bringing about astonishing cures. In Macedonia he treated King Perdiccas II, and in Abdera he was called upon to rid the city of a plague.

A pestilence was raging and out of control when he visited Athens. Noticing that blacksmiths were immune, Hippocrates reasoned that fire must be a remedy, and urged the building of huge bonfires. When the epidemic subsided, the grateful Athenians erected an iron statue in honor of their benefactor.

Historians give little credence to these and other stories of Hippocrates's genius. Perhaps they are right and the tales are but inventions of thousands of folk who believed themselves helped by his cures. But even if much of the stuff of which they are woven is only imaginary, fables cling to the great, and Hippocrates's greatness earned him the title by which we know him: Father of Medicine.

Undoubtedly Hippocrates was one of the many migratory Greek doctors. Like other craftsmen of that time, the doctors moved from place to place, selling their services where they were needed. Only the larger cities had resident physicians who were paid salaries raised by special taxes. Everywhere else, doctoring was done by wandering physicians. Like shoe-makers, blacksmiths, and other artisans, they knocked on doors or offered their services in the market place. Because they had to work in order to make a living, most of them were not highly regarded in Greek society.

The Greek doctor was neither licensed nor required to take a prescribed course in a medical school. Coming to each new town as a stranger, he had to prove himself on his merits. To gain his patient's trust, he told him very quickly what was wrong with him, what had to be done, and what would be the outcome of his illness. If time showed that he was right, he earned a reputation as a good doctor. If he proved to be wrong, it was dangerous for him to return to that town. Thus Hippocrates wrote:

"It appears to me a most excellent thing for the physician to

Hippocrates (460–375 B.C.)

cultivate prognosis; for by foreseeing and foretelling, in the presence of the sick, the present, the past, and the future, he will be the more readily believed to be acquainted with the circumstances of the sick; so that men will have confidence to intrust themselves to such a physician . . . . Thus a man will be the more esteemed to be a good physician, for he will be the better able to treat those aright who can be saved, from having long anticipated everything; and by seeing and announcing beforehand those who will live and those who will die, he will thus escape censure."

According to existing theory, disease was the result of a disturbed balance of the body's four humors, or fluids: blood, phlegm or mucus, yellow bile, black bile. Nature itself was a powerful healer, and the doctor, "nature's assistant," had only to help restore harmony among the humors by regulating the patient's habits and way of life, prescribing the right diet, fresh air, change of climate. Vegetable drugs made from a variety of herbs supplemented the diet. When diet and medicines failed, there was still the knife.

Equilibrium of the body humors could also be restored by opening a vein to drain out its diseased blood, or if there was an abscess, incising it so that the pus could escape.

The treatment of injuries incurred in battle or from accidents in sports was a large part of medical and surgical practice. What mattered was not so much what the surgeon knew about the functioning of internal organs as the skill he displayed in setting a fracture or reducing a dislocation.

Among the seventy Hippocratic treatises on medicine are the masterly presentations on fractures and dislocations. For a broken humerus (upper arm bone), "One should hang up a rod, in shape like a spade handle" suspended by a cord. "Seat the patient on a high stool and pass his arm over the rod so that it comes evenly under the armpit in such a position that the man can hardly sit and is almost suspended . . . . As to the surgeon, he should operate standing with one foot on some elevated support, adjusting the bone with the palm of his hands. The adjustment will be easy, for there is extension if it is properly managed."

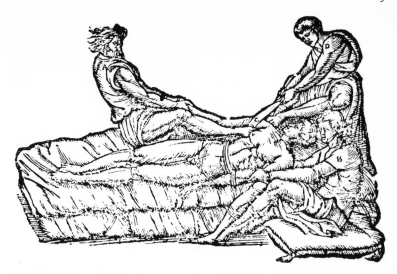

Hippocratic method of treating dislocated shoulder (from "Surgical Thought and Practice in Ancient Greece and Rome" by Benjamin Spector, M.D.)

There are detailed instructions for reducing a dislocation of the shoulder and of the lower jaw — procedures which are to some extent followed today. From the description of how to treat fractures and contusions of the skull, it is clear that the Hippocratic surgeons exhibited extraordinary insight into the nature and effects of such wounds. After "first inspection, without touching the patient . . . you should also ask the wounded man how he suffered the injury, and of what kind it was . . . further, that the man suffered vertigo [dizziness] and loss of sight, was stunned and fell down. Most cases have spasm of the parts on one side of the body; if the patient has the lesion on the left side of the head, spasm seizes the right side of the body; if he has the lesion on the right side of the head, spasm seizes the left side of the body. Some also become apoplectic and die in this state . . . ."

The practitioner is cautioned above all to determine which wounds are incurable, "which may be cured with difficulty, and which more readily. For it is the part of a prudent man first not to touch a case he cannot save, and not to risk the appearance of having killed one whose lot is but to die." But when the condition is grave though not absolutely hopeless, the patient's relatives are to be warned of the difficulty, "for then if the art is overcome by the malady, he will not appear to have been ignorant or mistaken." By the same token, the responsible doctor does not, "like a mountebank," exaggerate a mild case "in order to enhance his own achievement."

A section of the Hippocratic writings dealing with the control of hemorrhage includes the use of dry lint, wet sponges pressed down into the wound, and the application of lint soaked in vinegar. If these measures fail to stop the bleeding from blood vessels, then they "are to be tied in two places and cut across between" so that the two ends "coalesce" and the openings are closed. Only when this is not possible, as an extreme measure, "the blood vessels can be burnt with a red-hot iron."

Given in great detail, the Hippocratic methods of performing amputations, handling difficult labor, delivering a dead fetus, crushing bladder stones, treating intestinal hernias and other ailments show the extent to which the Greeks had learned the laws of nature through study, logic, and reason. Long before the development of modern science, Hippocrates and his followers wrested medicine from the bonds of superstition, mysticism, and priestcraft.

With all this, Hippocrates is best known for setting such high ethical standards for the medical profession that doctors today still take the Hippocratic oath, which says in part:

"In all my treatment I will strive so far as lies in my power for the benefit of the patients. And I will restrain myself from things which are injurious to them, or are likely in my opinion to do them harm."

Before their conquest of Greece, the Romans had lived without trained doctors for centuries, surgery being practiced by slaves, barbers, and a motley throng of quacks. After the conquest, wandering Greek physicians came to practice among the Romans and kept alive the only existing surgical knowledge. The greatest of these doctors was Galen.

The son of a cultured Greek, Galen was born in 130 A. D., in Pergamus, an ancient Greek city. His father, harrassed by a nagging wife who scolded him more mercilessly than Xanthippe did Socrates, gave him the name Galen, the Greek word meaning "calm." When the youth was eighteen years old, his father obeyed a dream that his son should be trained as a physician, and sent him to study under Straconicus and Satyrus, followers of Hippocratic medicine.

Two years later his father died, and at the age of twenty, Galen set out to see something of the world while continuing his studies. He traveled to Smyrna, Corinth, and Alexandria, spending nine years observing unfamiliar illnesses and new and different methods of treatment. The once famous university in Alexandria had gone downhill badly, and Galen found that an anatomist was no longer permitted to study diseased organs in humans. Nevertheless, he learned a great deal by dissecting and examining pigs, dogs, and monkeys.

Galen returned to Pergamus in the year 157, just in time to fill the vacant post of surgeon to the gladiators. During the first summer games, he earned a reputation for his excellent care of wounds and because of this also acquired a sizeable practice among private patients. When his appointment expired four years later, he went on to Rome.

Galen's home-town reputation didn't count in Rome. Cut-throat competition among the swarms of charlatans and quacks, who claimed to be specialists for different parts of the body, left little room for one more physician, and an immigrant at that. Galen bided his time, and made a point of becoming acquainted with some of his countrymen who also had settled in the capital. Among them was Eudemus, a distinguished philosopher. Eudemus became ill and was treated by the most famous doctor in Rome, only to grow worse and worse. In desperation he called in young Galen, who diagnosed the fever, accurately predicted the course of the illness, and prescribed the remedy. The patient recovered.

From then on, Galen's superior knowledge was recognized, fashionable Rome accepted him, and he became increasingly famous. The physicians who lost their patients to him were green with envy and tried to engage him in debate about his "school" of medicine. Galen arrogantly asserted his independence of any school and fought his professional enemies with fiery lectures and pamphlets. All the while he gained more patrons among the wealthy and the influential, including the son-in-law of Marcus Aurelius, Emperor of Rome.

Just when he was on the verge of becoming the emperor's personal physician, Galen suddenly left Rome and returned to his native land. His reason for turning his back on the coveted position of court physician remains unexplained. Some say he fled an epidemic which swept Rome that year, but we don't really know.

After he had become established in his old practice in Pergamus, he was called back to serve Marcus Aurelius, who was at war against the invaders threatening the northern boundaries of the empire. Despite the golden opportunity to dissect the bodies of those killed in battle, for some reason

Galen persuaded the emperor that he could serve him best as physician to the heir apparent. He stayed on in Rome for another thirty years, until his death in the year 199.

Besides practicing medicine and surgery, Galen lectured, taught and wrote voluminously on anatomy, physiology, medicine, and pharmacy. Much of what is known of the works of the Alexandrian anatomists is due chiefly to what Galen wrote of them. Although his dissections were done mostly on animals, he had an extensive knowledge of bone anatomy, accurately describing the bones and sutures of the skull, and the divisions of the vertebral column. He recognized that both arteries and veins carried blood (older Greeks thought the arteries carried air), and described a great many muscles, including those of mastication, the eyelids, and the muscles controlling the eyeball.

Galen considered himself a Hippocratist because he valued practical experience and sought to build an all-encompassing theory of medicine by fusing into one the prevailing conceptions of disease. One of the theories held that the body, like the universe, was composed of four elements — fire, air, water, and earth. The elements represented the qualities of the body: fire was hot, air was dry, water wet, and earth cold, and health consisted in preserving each of these qualities in its proper proportions. Disease resulted when the balance of the four qualities was disturbed.

Then there was the theory of humors. The yellow bile of the liver, on the right side, was supposed to balance the black bile of the spleen on the left side, and again an imbalance of the humors caused disease. A variation of this idea was that everyone belonged to one of four "temperaments" and a person who had more of one humor than of another naturally had the temperament for which that humor was responsible.

Claude Galen

Thus one who had more blood was supposed to be spirited and hopeful, with a *sanguine* temperament; a second, who had more of the yellow bile was bilious and called *choleric* or easily angered; a third, with more of the black bile, was dark-spirited or *melancholic;* the fourth was slow-moving and unresponsive or *phlegmatic.*

Galen thought that by somehow combining these theories into one he could provide a set of rules and formulas that any practitioner could follow in treating any and all conditions. Only an extremely vain man could have undertaken such a colossal conception based almost entirely on speculation.

As a practical physician, Galen was quite successful, but he possessed neither the genius for observation, the questioning mind, nor the devotion to the sick of Hippocrates. Without fully understanding what he observed, Galen would explain it in a way that fitted in with his dogmatic theory. Thus, not knowing that the blood from the right side of the heart gets to the left side by way of the lungs, he decided that it passed directly from the right to the left ventricle through imaginary pores in the partition. Having seen that wounds frequently festered, he taught that pus formation was necessary to their healing. This notion became known as "healing by second intention" and persisted for centuries, being a major factor in holding back the progress of aseptic surgery.

Toward the end of his life Galen wrote: "I have continued my practice on until old age, and never as yet have I gone far astray whether in treatment or in prognosis, as have so many other doctors of great reputation. If anyone wishes to gain fame through these . . . all that he needs is . . . to accept what I have been able to establish by zealous research."

Unquestioning persons, only too willing to forego the trouble of finding out for themselves, did indeed accept Galen as infallible. He became the final authority in medicine for over a thousand years, the Dark Ages of ignorance and superstition when science in Western Europe was at a standstill. If Hippocrates lit a candle to guide the path to research and the advancement of knowledge, Galen, by his overpowering dogma, almost snuffed it out.

CHAPTER THREE

The Sign of the Barber-Surgeon

The scene could be almost anywhere in Continental Europe, the time any year between 400 and 1400 A. D.

A barber-surgeon is passing through town, and will set up shop in the market place. It is widely rumored that his "wares" are many and varied: bloodletting, of course, but he also extracts teeth, removes cataracts as easily as warts, and cures hernias. Besides, they say he is an *expert* in "stones" — bladder stones, a common ailment in those days, because of the restricted diet.

The townspeople gather and the square is soon filled. A few have come as patients, with the faint hope of the hopeless for relief from their trouble and pain, yet fearful at the thought of the barber's knife and the perhaps greater pain of an operation. Some of the patients are here for bloodletting which they hope will stop the misery of aching joints or throbbing abscesses, or will rid them of the evil spirits that give them night sweats and hacking coughs. There are those among the onlookers who await with morbid interest the anticipated bloodcurdling screams and pain-contorted faces, but most are attending the spectacle as they would a circus.

At last the barber arrives and takes his place in the center of the crowd. He carries with him the usual sack containing instruments, vinegar, salves, herbs, poultices, and soporific sponges. But the true sign of his craft is the striped pole and basin: the stripe stands for the bandage he twists around the arm before cutting the vein, the basin is to catch the blood. To this day every barber displays the striped pole outside his shop, a symbolic reminder of the time when bleeding was an important part of his calling.

Among the wretched patients is one who is suffering with bladder stones and he has finally made up his mind to "go under the knife." Anything seems better than the excruciating pain. He presses forward, but the shrewd barber restrains him — he will be last on the list. The barber knows all too well the difficulties of this operation and does not intend to risk the patient's dying on the spot. The barber would then have to run for his life, for, according to official decree, if his patient dies he will be turned over to the dead man's relatives to do with as they like.

So as always he takes care of the less risky business first. With much fanfare he promises a quick recovery to each patient in turn, placing cupping glasses on the bared chest of one man, applying leeches to draw the blood from the legs of another. Judging the strength of the next victim, he punctures a blood vessel in his arm and lets just so much blood trickle into the basin.

The initiated among the crowd loudly applaud the barber's skill, and the curious newcomers follow each deft movement with keen interest. The wandering surgeon, finishing the other cases and sensing that he has won the crowd's confidence, is ready for the more spectacular procedure of removing the stone. But first he must get his fee, for how can he concentrate on the case and give the patient his best treatment, until he has been assured of proper payment?

Despite his pain, the man protests the high cost — where is the surgeon's sense of charity? But the surgeon isn't easily fooled by the patient's shabby clothes. The wealthy are always trying to get the fee reduced, he mutters, and announces for the benefit of the onlookers: "You have to pay for yourself and three other people, so that I may treat the poor for nothing."

Assured that he will feel no pain under the soporific sponge, the patient finally agrees to the fee and the surgeon quickly produces the sponge, previously treated with ground mandragora root and the juice of fresh hemlock. The patient is now on his back with his feet spread and tied upward. The sponge is soaked in water and placed over his nose to take his "very spirit away" and bring on sleep.

Then the lithotomist — stone surgeon — feels for the stone and works around it until it is close to the surface. A swift cut, and the stone is released. The surgeon loses no time in gathering up his equipment. His patient may not live very long, or if he escapes death from the operation, he may suffer more from its effects than from the stone itself. So with his striped pole and basin, the surgeon is speedily off to the next town.

———

Such was the state of surgery in the thousand years of darkness that followed the Graeco-Roman era of medicine. With the invasion from the North, Rome ceased to be a world power in the fifth century, and Greek learning and culture were banned by the Christian Church throughout Europe.

Hippocrates and his followers had freed medicine from religious rites, substituting careful bedside observation, but now the days of healing by miracles, amulets, charms, and sacred writings returned. Disease, no longer attributed to natural causes, was thought to be divinely inflicted: either the devil brought disease to make the faithful curse God, or God punished the sinful, purging their souls by affliction.

During the Middle Ages all medical and surgical knowledge might have been lost had not the classic treatises been translated into Arabic, Syrian, and Persian. The center of medical learning shifted to the Arab world, and in Western Europe the ancient teachings were forgotten. Medicine as an art could not compete with the miraculous power of relics, shrines, and the blessings of holy men; science could not get a start under the absolute authority of the Christian Fathers who were acknowledged as the sole possessors of knowledge.

As physicians, the clergy sought to cure disease by interceding with the powers to restore the patient to sound health. Different saints were prayed to for special remedies for various ailments: St. Attilia for the blind, St. Margaret for safe delivery of the newborn.

However, there was still room, even in this system of religious healing, for the lay physician. He needn't go to medical school, of course, for there were none. He had only to read Galen and follow his teaching exactly. Galen's rigid system of healing by rule fitted in well with the strict ecclesiastical authority, and his works had been translated into Latin, the official language of the Church. Only literate people who were able to read and write Latin could study and teach Galen. Among these were scribes connected with the monastery or others, like the physicians, who received their training largely from the clergy. Physicians studied the encyclopedic treatises of Galen, memorized every word, and engaged in endless debates about their meaning. For example, Galen had written that pus in wounds is necessary for their proper healing, so everything was done to irritate and infect them, despite the fact that it must have been observed that cleanliness rather than dirt helped in healing. The blind acceptance of Galen's errors led to stagnation of thought in medicine, and was also one of the reasons why the physician became separated from the surgeon.

Since the physician could diagnose a disease from a book without regard to actual symptoms, he soon saw no need for personally administering the cures, and such procedures as massaging, giving enemas, bandaging, opening abscesses, even bloodletting, became simple chores and not worthy of a doctor. They could be performed by illiterate helpers, apothecaries and barbers who could not read books but learned their craft by word of mouth from father to son, master to apprentice. Moreover, in the latter part of the Middle Ages the members of the clergy were forbidden by the Church to perform surgery, and increasingly it became a lowly, menial craft. As a medieval scribe wrote, a man had to have four qualities to become a surgeon: he must not be squeamish about foul smells, must be able to cut boldly like an executioner, and must know how to lie gracefully to his patient and obtain his fee. As a result, although many carried on their craft honestly, conscientiously, and with a degree of skill, the field was wide open to unscrupulous persons.

There were additional reasons why barbers in particular took over the work of surgeons. For one thing, they had the sharp instruments and the skill for cutting hair and performing other grooming operations. Thus barbers visited the monasteries regularly to shave the monks' heads and perform periodic bleeding that was required as a preventive health measure. Bloodletting, supposed to rid the body of sick humors, was the prevailing treatment for nearly every kind of disease. Soon the barber-surgeon's repertory included every type of operation.

The wealthy had their own personal barbers to shave them, cut their hair, and make and comb their wigs. The grooming also included giving baths, cutting nails, corns, and bunions, and treating skin eruptions, and when necessary, the barbers would extract teeth, dress wounds, and even amputate limbs. Through choice or necessity, some took to the road and became itinerant surgeons, wandering from town to town. If they managed to acquire a special skill — tooth pulling or bonesetting — they became "specialists" and could charge more for their services. Occasionally they were able to assume the role of physician and health adviser. In these ways they took over necessary functions that the learned physicians considered beneath their station.

As would be expected, professional jealousy and keen competition further divided the physician from the surgeon. If a physician happened to be first on a case, he would deride surgeons as ignorant, pompous fools who knew nothing of "reasoning," and would advise the distraught patient against calling one even if an operation was required: a surgeon knew nothing about treating the sick and delicate, and would only demand a fat fee. If the case became hopeless, he would piously recommend a surgeon, if possible some ruffian whom he could blame for the patient's death.

If a surgeon were called first, he would see to it that no physician ever saw the patient. What does a physician do, he would argue, but talk and purge, whether necessary or not?

While Central Europe was stagnating scientifically, Greek medicine was being assimilated and developed in the Near East. Alexandria, though no longer at its height, was still a center of learning in the seventh century A. D., when Paulus of Aegina, the last of the great Greek medical encyclopedists, carried the ancient learning and traditions to Egypt. Refugee scholars also emigrated to another intellectual center, Gundis-apora in Persia, where they met eminent Persian and Indian men of learning. Stimulated by this meeting of minds, the Arabian world, by the end of the ninth century, was making important new contributions to medical knowledge.

Interestingly enough, Arabian surgery was not separated from medicine: for example, Abucalsis, a leading authority, prepared an *Encyclopedia of Healing* which included three books dealing with *over a hundred* surgical instruments, new operations, and orthopedics. The most prominent of the Arabians was the physician-surgeon Avicenna, whose writings were so popular that he came to be known as "the Arab Galen."

While the Arabs utilized the knowledge of the Greeks, they were not merely imitators but introduced many innova-tions, including improvements in surgical instruments, sutur-ing, ligatures, obstetrics, and operations on the eye. At the same time, they still adhered to the doctrine of humors and temperaments, practiced bloodletting to drain off noxious humors, and their knowledge of anatomy was based on the dissection of animals.

Gradually the Arabian writings, good and bad, were brought to the West and translated into Latin, helping to raise the quality of medical practice in Europe. Among the trans-mitters of the new knowledge was Constantine, an African who traveled all over the Orient, and became a master of Eastern languages, and finally retired to the monastery at Monte Cassino, Italy, as a monk. Here he translated into Latin

Avicenna

the Arabian medical books he had brought with him, along with the works of Hippocrates and Galen.

At the time Constantine was making his notable contribution, a new medical school was beginning to flourish in Salerno, an Italian seaport and trading town which was a center for the exchange of western and eastern thought and influence. The school was the focus of a movement started by a group of physicians who were dissatisfied with the state of European medicine and ready to absorb the literature made available by Constantine. Together with the study of eastern practices, this represented an important turning point in the development of medicine and surgery in the western world. Although there was no human dissection, the importance of a knowledge of anatomy was recognized.

A century later, Frederick II, Emperor of South Italy and Sicily, helped to raise the standards of European medical education by approving a set of regulations "Concerning Medics." Three years as a pre-"medic" and five years as a "medic" with some study of surgery were required of every medical student. Upon certification by the professors at Salerno and after one year of apprenticeship under an experienced physician, the royal court granted the candidate "a license to practice." A surgeon could be licensed separately — with similar recommendations by his professors — if he could prove his skill in surgery, in the anatomy of human bodies, and his proficiency in medicine, "without which incisions cannot be safely made, nor fractures healed."

Medical centers were also established in northern Italy. In Bologna, William of Saliceto, the greatest of the early surgeons, introduced many surgical advances such as the suturing of cut nerves. He taught that severed arteries (from which the blood spurts) should be handled differently from veins, and warned against what he considered the excessive cauterization practiced by Arabian doctors, urging that the knife be used instead. In Padua, the practitioner Bruno was one of the first to recommend that wounds be kept clean and free from pus.

The newer ideas and methods of practice soon spread to other European centers, notably Montpellier and Paris. Here in France, the first surgeons' guild was established — the Confraternity of St. Cosmas. When the surgeons of Paris, who were better educated than the barber-surgeons, joined the guild, it became the officially recognized professional group.

The formation of the guild resulted in a sharp distinction between its members — Surgeons of the *Long* Robe — and the barber-surgeons — Surgeons of the *Short* Robe. This gave the former a standing comparable to that of physicians. More important, with this move came the recognition of the need for studying anatomy and medicine in preparation for surgery.

In Paris, Lanfranc, banished from Milan for political reasons, became a member of the surgeons' guild and by his conservative surgery helped to establish its reputation. He berated the barber-surgeons for their excessive operations for hernia (he recommended trusses instead) and warned against too free use of the knife for cataract. He also challenged the ability of the barber-surgeons even to let blood, and perform minor operations, insisting that surgery and medicine should be wedded as equal partners in the healing art.

Two other French surgeons — Henry de Mondeville and Guy de Chauliac — both of whom received their surgical training in Bologna, were prime movers in raising anatomy to the level of a scientific study in Italy. Both taught that medicine, surgery, and anatomy made up a healing trinity, and Guy de Chauliac said: "The surgeon who is ignorant of anatomy carves the human body as a blind man carves wood."

They introduced into France the practice of postmortem examination, at first for legal reasons only, and later for anatomical and medical knowledge. As a result, under the supervision of the Dean of the Medical School of the University and for the instruction of barber-surgeons, the first public human dissection in the history of Paris was performed.

—————

The exhausting Hundred Years War between England and France (1337-1453) was a serious setback to medical knowledge, as it was to all sciences except that of warfare. And with the recurring Black Death, the plague that killed off half of Europe, and against which medicine was helpless, the people clung more firmly to superstitions concerning the cause of disease. They reverted to magic, charms, potions, and powders as remedies. Surgeons again talked about "laudable pus" and deliberately promoted festering of wounds as an aid to healing. The introduction of gunpowder to Europe in the fourteenth century, and the consequent use of artillery and other firearms in warfare, led to greater use of cautery to remove "gunpowder poison" from wounds, just as bloodletting was supposed to cleanse the body of all other kinds of poisons.

With the end of the Hundred Years War, it became possible to devote men and material to other purposes: the great voyages of exploration leading to discovery of the New World, expansion and increased trade with the East. A demand for gold developed as a medium of exchange for spices, tea, silks, and all kinds of luxuries not found in Europe. The importance of the feudal manors declined as that of the trading centers grew. People began to work for wages, and guild masters became merchants.

Free trade and individual initiative challenged the restrictive authority of the manorial lord, the guilds, and even that of the Church. Inevitably, and supported by the discovery of new plants, animals, and diseases, the old precepts of medicine and surgery were also challenged, and people rebelled against the authority of the ancient books.

Where there is rebellion, there are always leaders. In the healing arts and in science, these were Paracelsus the doctor, Vesalius the anatomist, Paré the surgeon.

CHAPTER FOUR

Rebel Medic

For five years the renowned Swiss book printer, Johan Frobenius, had been suffering from an injury to his right leg, gangrene had set in, and amputation had been recommended. But having heard of the growing reputation of a doctor in the neighboring city, Strasbourg, the printer asked him to come to Basel. Paracelsus came, prescribed treatment, and saved his leg. He also cured Erasmus, the Rotterdam scholar, at the time a guest in the Frobenius home, of his kidney trouble. "I cannot offer thee a fee equal to thy art and learning," the grateful scholar had told the doctor. But Frobenius and he could and did show their gratitude by using their influence with the Town Council: Paracelsus was appointed to the vacant post of Municipal Physician. The appointment carried with it a professorship in the University of Basel, and early in the summer of 1527 the new professor announced his forthcoming course in medicine.

It was no routine announcement, for the course was a full program of medicine, and a new kind of medicine at that. Bluntly Paracelsus declared that the art of healing had fallen into decay, and that he, Paracelsus, would cleanse it of its

44

moldy ideas, "Not by following that which those of old taught, but by our own observation of nature, confirmed by extensive practice and long experience." Why were doctors making such horrible mistakes, he went on, if not because they were following the sterile teachings of Galen and Avicenna? Instead, they should be studying the secrets of nature, and in his course this is exactly what they would do.

"Day after day I publicly elucidate for two hours, with great industry and to the great advantage of my hearers, books on practical and theoretical medicine, internal medicine, and surgery, books written by myself. I did not, like other medical writers, compile these books out of extracts from Hippocrates or Galen, but in ceaseless toil I created them anew, upon the foundation of experience, the supreme teacher of things. . . . To express myself more plainly, let me say, by way of example, that I do not believe in the ancient doctrine of the complexions [temperaments] and the humours, which have been falsely supposed to account for all disease."

These bold but tactless words fell upon already hostile ears. The staid professors of the university faculty had not been consulted about his appointment, and resented it. Who was this maverick in their midst, an upstart without any formal credentials? Where were his diplomas and his doctor's cap? He looked more like a coachman than a physician with his broad-rimmed hat, knee-length coat and clanking sword! And even worse than his shocking manners, fiery tongue, and homely expressions, he spoke the vernacular, lecturing in the "vulgar" popular German instead of Latin, the language of the Church and the pundits.

Who, indeed, was this amazing man?

Wilhelm Bombast von Hohenheim, prodigal son of a noble

family of Swabia, decided to become a doctor. He opened his practice in Einsiedeln, the Swiss village on the road leading to the shrine of the Black Virgin, undoubtedly thinking of the potential patients among the thousands of worshippers who regularly made the pilgrimage past his house.

He soon married the young nurse who was in charge of the hospital at Einsiedeln, and their son, born in 1493, was christened Philip. The father added the name Theophrastus in memory of the Greek philosopher whom he admired, and because of the color of the small, frail boy's hair, he was also called Aureolus, the Greek word for "Goldilocks."

His mother's tender care nursed Philip through a sickly childhood, and his father's interest in nature gave the boy his first insight into the world of plants, rocks, and minerals. Wilhelm taught Philip to read, and introduced him to the practice of healing when he was hardly out of his boyhood.

In 1502, Frau Hohenheim died, and Dr. Hohenheim moved to Villach, a mining town in Carinthia where he became Municipal Physician. The move promised a better living for himself and the boy, not only because he was assured of a salary, but also because the miners were better able to pay a doctor's fee than the weary pilgrims who had nothing but the clothes on their backs. Dr. Hohenheim may have had other reasons for leaving Einsiedeln: his wife's sudden passing cut his ties with her native town, and in the larger town of Villach, his son could look forward to a better future.

In Villach young Hohenheim attended the Benedictine Abbey school. The town also offered another type of education in the nearby smelting works and mining school, and while still a boy he had learned more chemistry than even medical students knew in those days. Johann, the alchemist at the mining school, introduced him to the secret art of transmuting metals. But to be a doctor like his father, which was his ambition, he needed more formal schooling, and after learning the arts at the University of Vienna, he went on to study medicine at the University of Tübingen where his father had studied. Before long the boy became dissatisfied with learning anatomy from a teacher who read it out of a book. Perhaps in another university he could get his hands on a cadaver and be able to work in a laboratory like Johann's with its crucibles, furnaces, retorts, and pelicans. He joined a group of wandering students who went from university to university, traveling on dusty roads from town to town to sip at the fount of knowledge wherever they found it.

But each new place he visited only added to his disillusionment with formal education. Everywhere teaching was entirely from books, argumentation took the place of examination of patients, the study of anatomy from dissection was scant and sporadic, and the theories of disease were still Galenic.

Some time during his travels Philippus Theophrastus Aureolus Bombastus von Hohenheim chose to discard his name in favor of "Paracelsus." This was not because he was not proud of his origin. He was very much attached to his family, who he said were not "woven of silk" but of "coarse linen." Perhaps the change of name denoted his admiration for the famous Roman doctor Celsus, who was supposed to have laid aside Galen's humor theory to prescribe specific remedies according to the patient's symptoms.

Paracelsus had already seen a great deal of practical bedside healing by his father, and had studied science at first hand in the fields and mines. What could the stodgy university professors teach him about the true causes of disease, about remedies, about surgery? He made up his mind to seek other sources of knowledge, and it didn't really matter what they were. Anyone with experience would be an improvement — midwives, barber-surgeons, apothecaries, abbots, miners, metal craftsmen, even gypsies, sorcerers, quacks, and old women.

So he left the stuffy atmosphere of the universities and practiced medicine while on the road. In some places he joined warring armies and treated the wounded and maimed. His travels took him through Italy, France, Spain, Portugal, England, and Scotland. He went north to the Scandinavian countries, east to Poland, Lithuania, and Russia, and south to Constantinople and Alexandria. For years he lived the life of an itinerant, working in mines and on farms, and practicing medicine where he could, learning, writing, and teaching the students he picked up from time to time along the way. Above all, he tried to learn from everyone he met.

He talked with doctors, surgeons, craftsmen, clergymen, scholars, and alchemists. Everywhere he visited mineral springs, which always held an interest for him. Inquiring about ailments in different regions, he became aware of the effect of surroundings on disease, learned new therapies, and developed his own treatments and theories.

He ridiculed the concoctions made up of scores of ingredients that were prescribed as drugs by the doctors of the time. One component neutralized the other, he argued: use simple remedies, and most of all find out what each specific ingredient does in the body. His extensive knowledge of minerals led him to the use of metals in the treatment of disease. In addition to laudanum (opium), he tried gold, copper, sulfur, lead, mercury, antimony, and other compounds. "The object of alchemy is not to make gold but to prepare medicines," he taught.

Since he carefully watched the effects of his treatment and

Paracelsus

knew so much chemistry, he was often successful in bringing
about cures where other doctors, following by rote the same
old prescriptions, had failed. On the battlefield he often saved
a limb that others were ready to amputate. By washing the
wound clean and by gentle handling of the patient, he per-

mitted nature's healing powers to work. But mainly he wanted to know the why and how of the disease, constantly trying to answer questions that still puzzle doctors. Why did people become sick? What caused different diseases in different people? What was aging and death?

After many years of wandering, Paracelsus began to look around for a place to settle down, to practice what he had learned, to teach his new doctrine, to remake the theory and practice of medicine as he saw it. After visiting his father, still in Villach, he went on to Salzburg, and had no sooner begun to practice there when the War of the Peasants broke out. Always a man of the people, and almost constitutionally opposed to existing authority, he actively sided with the peasants in their fight for land, and was soon arrested. Even though he was released after only a short imprisonment, he was no longer welcome in Salzburg, and once more moved on. Arriving in Strasbourg where he hoped to publish his writings and perhaps join the school of surgery, he applied for citizenship and was duly entered in the Burgher's Roll as a citizen. The year was 1526, and he was thirty-three years old.

Within a year all Europe was talking about the wonderful cures of Paracelsus. His great skill in surgery and his success in curing gout and kidney disease brought his name to the attention of Frobenius and Erasmus, and in 1527, as we have seen, he was summoned to Basel.

His life-long dreams seemed to be coming true. At last he would be able to teach at a university and, with his students, free medicine from the ancient dogmas that were paralyzing all original thought and attempts at progress. Also he hoped that his friendship with Frobenius would lead to the printing of his books, so that others could share the experience he had acquired. "My travels have developed me; no man becomes a master at home, nor finds his teacher behind the stove. Sicknesses wander here and there the whole length of the world. If a man wishes to understand them, he must wander too. A doctor must be an alchemist, he must see mother earth where the minerals grow."

A professorship at the Basel University was just what he wanted to enable him to bring his ideas to the medical world. And the rebel doctor hoped that at last he would be permitted to teach without the opposition he had encountered from academicians everywhere else. But his hopes were soon shattered.

The announcement by Paracelsus of his program was taken by the faculty as an open declaration of war. Then, as if he had not flouted faculty authority enough, the intruder had lectured in German, the language of the people. He invited to his lectures barbers, alchemists, and anyone else who might profit from them, thus breaking all precedent. The dons raised their hands in horror at this heresy and forbade him the use of the lecture hall. But Frobenius interceded, and Paracelsus was permitted to continue.

At first his classes were well attended. Here was something new and intriguing, an innovator who refused to parrot the classics, who lectured about diseased organs, told how to diagnose ailments from the pulse rate and analysis of the urine, discussed the preparation of new remedies and the treatment of wounds and abscesses. Alarmed at his success, the faculty began to gather its strength and, looking for allies, found them in the very enemies Paracelsus created for himself.

Among them were the town's doctors Paracelsus was denouncing: "These calves think themselves great masters, for did they not go through the examination at Nuremberg?" he

scoffed. Was it a crime for the sick to contradict these bung-
lers who tortured them? The apothecaries also had an axe to
grind: this impostor, in his capacity as town physician, insisted on inspecting their compounds which he scorned as
"foul broths."

Even his students turned against him. In their desire to
become respected doctors they were frightened by his advanced ideas, for what if the offended professors failed to
grant them their diplomas? Could they afford to support this
heretic who cast doubts on the infallibility of Galen, and who
at the celebration of the Feast of St. John, the healer, flung
Avicenna's *Canons of Medicine* into the bonfire and cried out
to the students: "In these flames and smoke all misery shall be
carried away."

One morning a satirical verse aimed at Paracelsus was
found on all the doors of the university and of the churches.
It could only have been written by a student, and Paracelsus
became bitter, for now it was clear that he could not count on
the new generation. He turned to the Town Council for help
and protection, but this gesture was half-hearted. What good
would it do to punish the students, the very ones he had hoped
would carry the torch of reform?

The faculty now plotted to speed his expulsion, and were
encouraged by the death of Frobenius, who suffered a stroke
while on a horseback ride to Frankfort. Although the trip had
been taken against Paracelsus's advice, his days in Basel were
numbered, for he had lost his only influential friend. Not yet
satisfied, his enemies prepared a trap that would bring his brief
career in the city to an abrupt end.

Called to the cathedral to treat a canon, a man of wealth,
Paracelsus cured him and accordingly asked for 100 guldens,
the customary fee paid by rich men. The canon refused to

pay the agreed fee, offering only six guldens, and Paracelsus duly brought him into court. Not only did the verdict unexpectedly go against the doctor, but the judge went out of his way to heap unheard-of abuse on him. There was only one thing to do, and one night in February, 1528, Parcelsus left Basel. A lonely man, but still convinced of his great mission, he again became a wanderer.

Forbidden to teach from the lectern and the amphitheatre, he was more than ever determined to write and get his message onto the printed page. He called one book *Paragranum*, another *Paramirum*. No one knows what these names mean, except that this eccentric but earnest man used the same form in his own name, Paracelsus.

In these writings he sets forth his four basic principles of medicine: knowledge of nature, astronomy, chemistry, and virtue. Who could be a better teacher than nature herself if we examine her and force her to give up her secrets? By the principle of astronomy, Paracelsus meant that just as the stars are governed by certain cosmic laws, mankind is subject to environment and historic events. To understand the workings of the body, we must study also chemistry because life is essentially a composite of chemical reactions: "Nature is the arch-chemist and we must imitate her, otherwise we are no more than kitchen sluts." Virtue in medicine was the devotion of the physician to his patient and to the highest ethics of his calling.

Paracelsus was the first writer to discuss such new remedies as mercury, antimony, lead, gold, potassium sulfate, arsenic, tartaric acid, and guaiac wood. He expounded on the curative values of mineral waters and health resorts and wrote separate treatises on mental diseases, disorders of the liver and kidneys, and the treatment of wounds and surgical diseases.

But he was no more successful with publishers than with the university authorities. During his lifetime all of his writings were refused publication except for a short article on the value of mineral waters in the treatment of syphilis and one major work on wounds. Only after the author had been dead for nearly half a century were some of his works printed. Much of his writing was undoubtedly lost, and some remained in manuscript form.

For thirteen years after he fled from Basel, Paracelsus continued his restless traveling. Poor, lonely, hungry, and in rags he dragged his weary body over endless dusty roads, never knowing where he would rest his head at nightfall. But he never faltered in his fearless crusading — healing the sick, searching for new remedies, preaching his ideas and putting them down on paper. All his life he fought the "old and obstinate dogs who will learn nothing new and are ashamed to recognize their folly."

In 1541, sick, worn, and old before his time, he returned to Salzburg. Though he was only forty-eight, he knew that the end had come, and three days before he died called a notary to draw up his will. His material belongings were few: some coins and jewels, given him by wealthy patients, which he left to a few friends; his manuscripts, which were entrusted to a barber-surgeon, in whose hands they would be safer than with a stuffy doctor. The rest of his possessions were bequeathed to the poor because he had been one of them. He died on September 24, 1541, and was buried in the cemetery of the Hospital of St. Sebastian in Salzburg. The engraving on the simple stone reads: "Here is buried Philippus Theophrastus, distinguished Doctor of Medicine, who with wonderful art cured dire wounds, leprosy, gout, dropsy, and other incurable diseases of the body."

Paracelsus was indeed one of the great practitioners and medical thinkers of all time. He clearly saw that Galen's system of the four humors restricted or prevented any real understanding of the composition of the human body. He taught that every organ consists of three principles: the part that burns, the part that doesn't burn, and the volatile. Sulfur, mercury, and salt enter into every organ. And some "vital" principle holds them together.

He is remembered even more for introducing chemicals as medicines, for putting alchemy to work in healing. And historically his greatest contribution was his endless asking of bold questions and reaching for their answers. By his courage he made it possible to sweep aside the curtain, drawn for a thousand years, on all that was stagnant and stifling in the ancient teaching about health and disease.

It is ironic that with all of Paracelsus's experience, work, and sacrifice, it was a contemporary who succeeded in his own day, whereas Paracelsus failed to change men's ideas of medicine and surgery. . . .

CHAPTER FIVE

Renaissance in Anatomy

On the last day of the year 1514, Andreas Vesalius was born in Brussels. Andreas came from a line of eminent physicians, dating back to his great-great grandfather, Peter Vesalius, who had written a treatise on Avicenna. It is said that the name of Vesalius was adopted from the town of Vesel in the Duchy of Cleves, in the Low Countries, to which the family traced its beginnings.

Andreas was named for his father, who had been apothecary to Margaret of Austria and later to her nephew, the Hapsburg Emperor Charles V, whom he accompanied on his military expeditions. Andreas's mother had great hopes that her son would add further honor to the family name by following the medical tradition of his ancestors. She treasured their writings and loved to tell Andreas the stories of their loyal service to the sovereigns.

Andreas went to school in the neighboring city of Louvain. Louvain University, where his great-grandfather had been a teacher, was by then a century old and had won a proud reputation. Here Andreas took a course in literature, obtaining a thorough grounding in Latin and a smattering of Greek,

Hebrew, and Arabic. But his interest in languages was overshadowed by his early and endless curiosity about the structure of living things, no doubt influenced by his mother's recounting of the family's achievements in medicine. Even as a young boy he was convinced that anatomy was not to be learned from books, and he performed dissections on mice, rats, cats, dogs, and "our weasels," the little ermine-furred animals represented on the family coat of arms.

At the age of nineteen, determined to follow in his forefathers' footsteps, Andreas started his medical studies at the University of Paris. Many renowned professors of medicine had been attracted to the French capital and had revived Galen's writings in the original to correct the distortions they had suffered by translation into the Eastern languages. The most popular of the teachers was Jacobus Sylvius, whose name is still given to parts of the brain that he discovered.

Like Vesalius, Sylvius was a student of languages, but during his apprenticeship to a Parisian practitioner he had learned anatomy, and before long he was lecturing on Hippocrates and Galen. His popularity aroused the envy of the other members of the faculty of the university and they protested his right to teach, demanding: "Who is this intruder without a medical degree?"

So Sylvius went to the University of Montpellier, obtained his doctor's cap, and returned to Paris. This time the faculty insisted that he must get a bachelor's degree. He was fifty years old, but he fulfilled this requirement too, and resumed his lectures before enthusiastic audiences numbering in the hundreds.

His success at teaching was due not only to his eloquence but also to the fact that he taught anatomy with human cadavers, probably for the first time in France, and botany with

Sylvius

living plants. But he could not rid himself of blind adherence to Galen's word. If a dissection plainly showed some structure to be different from what the master had described, the cadaver was wrong, not Galen. Galen wrote that the thigh bone was curved. When Sylvius found it to be straight, he declared it was because the shape of the bone had been changed since Galen's time by the tight pants men wore. He depended so much on Galen's book that in classroom dissection he often was unable to locate certain parts of the body. One day, after the professor had failed to find them, his students showed him the valves at the exit of the large arteries from the heart.

Vesalius listened and learned, but complained that there was still too much lecturing and useless debating and not enough dissection. And what little dissection there was, was done by ignorant barbers. He wrote that one of his professors, Guinterius, never had used a knife on a cadaver. "I would not mind having as many cuts inflicted on me as I have seen him make either on man or other brute (except at the banqueting table)," the critical youth wrote of his teacher.

In anatomy classes the barber wielded the knife, as large as a butcher's cleaver, a demonstrator pointed to the parts of the body with a long rod, and the professor sat on a raised platform from which he delivered his lecture. More often there was no cadaver in the amphitheatre, and when they did have a human body on the table, the dissections were carried out for only three days, leaving no time for the study of arteries, veins, or nerves. Bones were studied individually, not in a jointed skeleton, and without relation to each other or to the muscles.

Though Guinterius and Sylvius were the most advanced and enlightened teachers of that day, they were not what young Vesalius had hoped for in Paris. He was not only critical, but at times he was also so bold as to push the barbers aside, take the knife himself, and carry out the dissection as he thought it should be done. While Guinterius praised the young Belgian for his zeal and his skill in locating muscles, arteries, and nerves, Sylvius, an avaricious and bitter man, furiously resented his impudence.

But Vesalius did not mind his professor's disapproval. With each rebuff, he became all the more determined to learn the intricacies of the human body. "Never would I have been able to accomplish my purpose in Paris, if I had not taken the work into my own hands," he later wrote. He studied every bone he could get hold of, and cut up dog after dog.

One of his ambitions was to collect enough different human bones to join them into a complete skeleton. With other students whom he enlisted to help in his search, Andreas haunted the Cemetery of the Innocents. Night after night they visited the area where the bodies of executed criminals were heaped without benefit of burial, always having to fight off hungry dogs whose noses had led them there. It was a risky pursuit, but the daring Vesalius got what he was after and learned the parts of the skeleton so well that he could describe every bone blindfolded.

His knowledge won him the respect and admiration of both professors and students, and in no time he was able to demonstrate dissection in class. No part of the body was neglected. He laid open the abdomen and dissected the organs usually ignored by the barbers.

Suddenly the War of 1536-37 broke out when Charles V invaded Provence, now part of France. Vesalius, an imperial subject, had to return immediately to the Low Countries without finishing his education. He returned to the University of Louvain accomplished in the art of dissection and with a burning desire to use his skill to learn more of the secrets of the body.

With a physician friend he set out one night for the gallows outside the city walls. Here he found a prize, a complete skeleton held together by the ligaments and enough of the tendons to show how the muscles were attached to the joints! It was what was left of a notorious robber selected for more than the usual punishment of hanging: he had been tied to a stake and burned alive by a slow fire. The scav-

Vesalius dissecting in secret

engers, this time buzzards instead of dogs, had feasted on the roasted flesh, but had left behind — a weird sight under the light of the moon — a fresh, white, completely jointed skeleton, such as the young anatomist had tried for years to put together from the bones of many different bodies.

With the help of his friend, Andreas climbed to the top of the gallows, detached the skeleton, and carried it safely home. Except for a missing kneecap, a finger, and one foot, he now had his coveted treasure. The next night he again stole out of the city and after a long search among the remains at the site of the gallows, found the missing bones and returned safely through another gate.

Shortly afterwards, these secret after-dark expeditions were made unnecessary. Times and ideas had changed; the Burgomaster of Louvain made plenty of dissection material available, and Vesalius soon gave the first public anatomy lecture held in Louvain in eighteen years. This time he ran into a different kind of trouble. In his lecture he made some remarks about the seat of the soul in the cadaver, highly offending the clergy. While there was no formal charge of heresy, the suspicion continued to hover over his head.

Vesalius's systematic dissection of the human body was an historic break with medical tradition and the practices of his own time. He was already far ahead of his ancestors, and in the family tradition he soon embarked on a writing career. His first work was a translation into readable Latin of the ninth book of Rhazes, a celebrated Arab physician of the ninth century. This volume, used as a textbook in medieval times, described treatments for all parts of the body, to which Vesalius added many notes and explanations, illustrated with drawings of medicinal plants, and including contributions to *materia medica*. Vesalius believed that many of Rhazes's remedies had been unknown to the Greeks.

After publication of the book in 1537, Vesalius went to Venice. In this enlightened city he encountered no restrictions on the study of anatomy, and was able to branch out into the use of herbs as medicines, experimenting particularly with chinaroot, an East Indian shrub that he advocated as a remedy for pleurisy. In Venice he began to practice minor surgery, including bloodletting with leeches and by the opening of veins. For the first time he used the *popliteal* vein in the leg, judiciously avoided by the barbers because of its size. It was also in Venice that he met Jan Stephan van Calcar, an artist in the workshop of the famed Titian, who later helped him to illustrate his major anatomical work.

From Venice he went on to Padua, where he was awarded the degree of Doctor of Medicine "with highest distinction."

Thus at the end of the year 1537 Vesalius had earned all the rights and privileges of a graduate physician, and was immediately appointed Professor of Surgery to teach anatomy at the University of Padua. This was the first time that a professor had held a chair in anatomy as a separate subject.

Bent on making improvements in teaching, his first innovation was to act as lecturer, demonstrator, and dissector all in one. Having no use for ignorant barbers, he chose students as assistants, and saw to it, by whatever means, that there was no dearth of dissection material.

———

Let us go to the University of Padua, in the year 1537-1538, and look in upon a large wooden hall built like an amphitheatre, with rows of benches rising from the center of the room. In the center stands a long table on which the cadaver is to be placed. Under the table is a basket holding individual bones, and suspended to the right there is a fully articulated skeleton. At least five hundred students, teachers, and distinguished guests — government officials, the clergy, and other learned persons — have assembled to watch the renowned Belgian professor demonstrate a human dissection.

Professor Vesalius begins by lecturing on the need for direct anatomical observations on both animals and humans — the only way to obtain an understanding of body structure. Explaining that the main divisions of the body are the same whether in a pig, a dog, or a lamb, he proceeds to outline the arrangement of the tissues — skin, connective tissues, fat, and muscles — as each layer is peeled away in one of these animals. Then he points to the attachment of muscles, by their tendons, to the bones and cartilages at the joints. The body cavities are next laid open and the various organs located in relation to one another. This is all preliminary to the painstaking anatomical study of the human body.

Speaking and pointing to the structures at the same time, he presents drawings for greater clarity, sometimes sketching as he goes along. Now and then he illustrates a structure by outlining on the skin the underlying parts, tracing on the scalp with ink the location of the skull sutures.

A startling innovation is his vast array of dissecting knives and other instruments of different shapes and sizes, very similar to the ones used today. Never use scissors in dissection, he points out, for what you cut away with scissors is lost in its proper relationship to other structures.

Then a cadaver is brought in and placed on the table. Even for the initiated this is an exciting moment, for human dissection is not yet a routine affair. The professor follows the same method as with the animal, systematically demonstrating each division of the body in regular order. Only one cadaver will be available for this course, so he dissects the muscles and ligaments in one limb, and leaves the other to illustrate the course of the nerves, arteries, and veins.

Vesalius uses his knives, hooks, probes, and needles with great dexterity so as to separate but not sever the structures under study; in a good dissection it should be possible to lay each part back in its proper place when the job is complete. Nerves and delicate blood vessels are separated from the attached tissues with needles or, if need be, with fingernails, and lifted on a thread. Only in this way can the structure in its entirety be followed accurately.

The professor is indefatigable, for the demonstration continues for nearly the whole of every day for several weeks until the dissection is complete. One must work steadily, and in the winter, to prevent the disintegration of the tissues. His presentation is no less vivid than the excitement of unfolding and relating each part of the anatomy. He remarks now and then on the workings of the organ under dissection, and on the probable cause of disordered function in disease. But he wastes little time on theoretic discussion and speculation, insisting that our knowledge is increased only by what can be proved.

———

The fame and reputation of the young and vibrant professor brought him invitations to conduct public anatomical demonstrations in other cities. For two years in succession — 1539 and 1540 — Vesalius was called to Bologna, where he gave his courses to large, enthusiastic audiences. Wherever he found that Galen's descriptions, based largely on animal dissections, were not borne out by the human dissection, he boldly pointed out the mistakes.

Vesalius was a genius in the science of anatomy, and he was also a great teacher. He knew the value of charts, diagrams, and pictures. If you can draw what you see, you have seen accurately. In turn, what you draw of the details of a structure assists others to find them in the body. To help the beginning student in anatomy, Vesalius prepared a set of loose-leaf anatomical plates based on his demonstrations. The skeletons were drawn by van Calcar; the other plates, showing the heart and large blood vessels, the circulation to the liver, and the organs of reproduction, he drew himself.

The accuracy and naturalness of the drawings, and the skill with which these rare plates were executed, still astound modern anatomists. But *The Tabulae Anatomicae* were only the prelude to Vesalius's masterwork, which he began in 1539. After three years of tireless work, the *Fabrica* — its

Vesalius and dissected arm (from the Fabrica)

full title was *De Corporis Humani Fabrica Libri Septum* (Seven Books on the Structure of the Human Body) — was ready to go to press. This book, so different from the old authorities, was the first major work of modern science, containing drawings and descriptions of the whole human body as revealed by dissection. It was a labor of infinite skill and devotion to scientific truth. For the first time, meaningful illustrations clarified and enhanced the printed word.

The pages and plates were dispatched to Johannes Oporinus in Basel, Switzerland, the chief publishing center of Europe. Before turning to printing, Oporinus had been a classical scholar and former medical student in the household of the eccentric Paracelsus. He was also a dear friend to whom Vesalius felt he could entrust his masterpiece of science and creative art. Early in 1543, Vesalius went to Basel to personally superintend the printing, just as he had painstakingly directed the work of the artist, to assure the utmost faithfulness in every detail of the drawings.

In that same year, 1543, the monumental work came off the press, bearing a dedication to Charles V.

Vesalius's book follows the same plan as his systematic dissections, the first part dealing with the bones and joints, and including drawings of the different shapes of human skulls and a comparison of the skull of man with that of the dog and other animals. In the second part, Vesalius succeeded, with the eye and skill of an artist, in representing the muscles in their normal state of contraction. This required far more knowledge than that needed for a mere representation of dead anatomical structures. The third to seventh parts were on the veins and arteries, the nerves, the organs of nutrition and generation, the heart and lungs, the brain and sense organs.

In 1943, the four-hundredth anniversary of Vesalius's

grand work was celebrated the world over. Since he laid down his scalpel and pen, anatomists have learned little that needs to be changed or added to his masterpiece. Yet this is only part of what we owe to the master. Medieval physicians and surgeons, relying on what was in Galen's books, had been unable to make any real progress in anatomy. Vesalius, believing only what he saw, not only corrected many of Galen's errors but also infused into anatomy and other sciences a creative spirit of questioning.

Galen wrote that there were two bones in the lower jaw; Vesalius found only one. Galen denied the existence of marrow in the bones of the hand; Vesalius proved it was there. These are but two of the numerous corrections with which Vesalius challenged the authority of Galen and taught anatomists to learn by direct observation. This is not to say that he denied the entire Galenic heritage; only where his own eyes showed the master to be wrong did Vesalius insist on the truth of his observations.

Commenting on Galen's "pores" in the wall dividing the right and left chambers of the heart, Vesalius wrote:

". . . not long ago [I] should hardly have ventured to differ from that Prince of Physicians by so much as a finger's breadth. As for the dividing wall, or septum, between the ventricles . . . the student of anatomy should consider carefully that it is equally thick, compact, and dense, with all the rest of the cardiac substance enclosing the left ventricle. And accordingly, notwithstanding what I have said about the pits in this situation . . . I still do not see how even the smallest quantity of blood can be transfused, through the substance of the septum, from the right ventricle to the left."

His great work complete, Vesalius found himself in the midst of a fierce battle: "How could anyone be so brazen or so foolish as to contradict the established authority of Galen?"

While his students were mostly on his side, the older

professors roared with anger or more subtly ridiculed his innovations. There were those who just shrugged their shoulders in cynical disbelief, but some of his critics were powerful and outspoken: his old teacher, Sylvius, called him a madman who was poisoning Europe with his teachings.

The *Fabrica* was accepted in Germany, Holland, and England, but in Padua the storm raged. Some of his students turned against him, openly reviling him in his anatomy lectures at the university. Bitter at those who had sat at his feet, and now had their hands on his throat, Vesalius left Padua for Pisa, then Bologna. But everywhere in Italy he was opposed by those who were unable or unwilling to follow his teachings. Discouraged and angered by what seemed to him futile fights and pointless arguments, Vesalius burned the manuscript of his new book on the practice of medicine, and at the age of thirty he left Italy.

He had been offered and now accepted the quiet post of personal physician to King Charles V of Spain, whose kingdom extended from South America to the Zuyder Zee in Holland. Vesalius accompanied the king in battle and became experienced in military surgery. In the intervals of peace, he served as physician to the imperial household in Madrid.

His withdrawal from the scene temporarily silenced his enemies, but the restless seeker for truth was not satisfied with this secluded life. He was held in great esteem by the Spanish Court for his service to Charles and later to his son Philip, and for performing an operation that saved the life of Philip's son Don Carlos. But fame as a surgeon only was not enough. As he said, in Madrid he could not lay a hand on a skull, much less do a dissection in the open, for under Philip's reign human dissection was taboo. Defying the edict, Vesalius continued working in secret, longing for the free golden days he had known in Italy.

One day in 1564, at the height of his court success, he suddenly disappeared, turning up in Venice with plans for publishing a new book. The mere announcement of this was enough to start the old battle over again. Sylvius was dead, but the controversy over Galen still raged, and Vesalius was now attacked by Fallopius, another of his former students.

Here the record is unclear, but the story is told that Vesalius was requested by the parents of a young man (some say a woman) who had just died, to open the body and determine the cause of death. As soon as he made the incision he found the heart still beating. He was immediately accused of both murder and heresy. But his life was saved by the King of Spain, who interceded for him on the condition that his former court physician make a pilgrimage of repentance to the Holy Land. And so he went to Jerusalem and made his atonement.

In the meantime, Vesalius was invited back to Padua to occupy the chair left vacant by the death of his one-time protegé, Fallopius. He set sail in the fall of 1564, but the ship was wrecked and Vesalius, at the age of fifty, died from exhaustion on the island of Zante in the Mediterranean Sea.

Andreas Vesalius, Father of Anatomy, had made his historic contribution by the time he had reached his thirtieth birthday. Thwarted for years, he persevered to strike a deadly blow at the authority of Galen, to chart the future path of research in anatomy, physiology, and surgery, to revolutionize the teaching of the structure of the human body, and to wipe out the stagnant past. And in so doing, he left a monument that has survived the centuries — the *Fabrica* — the first of the major building blocks in the structure of modern surgery.

CHAPTER SIX

Prince of Surgeons

If you should ever happen to visit the city of Laval in France you will find a bronze statue by Pierre Jean David, erected in 1840. If you read the inscription, you will find that it was paid for by contributions from the French people, in memory of a surgeon who died two hundred and fifty years before.

How many statues there are of generals and statesmen, and how few have been raised to honor doctors, particularly with money raised by popular subscription. But Ambroise Paré was no ordinary surgeon.

Ambroise was born in 1510 in the village of Bourg Hersent, which later became part of Laval. His father was valet and barber to the nobleman Sieur de Laval, and an older brother was a master surgeon in the city of Vitré. Evidently Ambroise's father wanted him to follow the same craft, for he sent him to live with a priest in order to learn Latin, the traditional language of doctors. But instead, the priest put the boy to work in the garden and stable, and neglected to give him the promised lessons. Ambroise was then apprenticed to a barber-surgeon, who probably taught him little but the art of bloodletting.

The story goes that one day the boy watched an itinerant surgeon perform a lithotomy, and was so impressed that he determined that some day he would go to Paris and study under the masters. But first he probably went to Vitré to study surgery with his brother.

He remembered that his brother was especially clever at exposing beggars who feigned serious illness or injury to make people feel sorry for them. One day they came upon such an impostor, who was displaying a gangrenous arm to all passers-by. The surgeon was suspicious. Opening the poor wretch's cloak, he found two sound arms and a third, hung from his neck, that had belonged to a criminal recently executed. The beggar was taken to court, publicly whipped, and run out of town.

After some time in Vitré, when Paré was about twenty-two, he at last got to Paris, not to study with a master surgeon, but as apprentice to a barber-surgeon. In the Paris hierarchy of medicine, the barber-surgeons were the lowest of three ranks. At the top were the physicians, jealous of their membership in the University faculty, which gave them the right to decide who should and who should not practice medicine. Below them were the Surgeons of the Long Robe, members of the Guild of Saint Côme (Cosmas), patron of surgeons. They applied ointments and plasters and used cautery, but considered actual operating beneath their position. This they left to the barber-surgeons, who did all of the bleeding, cupping, and leeching, and were always ready to undertake more difficult operations. What they may have lacked in skill they often compensated for in daring, and some even became specialists: the lithotomists who removed stones, the incisors who operated on hernias, and the *rabouteurs*, expert bonesetters. The barber-surgeons also did the dissecting in anatomy courses,

From a seventeenth-century painting: The Surgeon

which taught them practical anatomy and helped them to treat wounds, set fractured bones, and practice surgery.

Not knowing Latin, Paré could not read the classic texts, but instead used the works of Guy de Chauliac in a French version. Whether he decided he had learned all that the barber-surgeon could teach him, or left his apprenticeship for other reasons, is not known. But he now began work as a "companion surgeon" in the Hôtel-Dieu, the great Paris hospital founded in the seventh century. The hospital was on the left bank of the Seine, right on the river's edge, and the stench of the polluted water penetrated the dank walls of the old building. It was hardly an ideal place for people to get well in. The victims of the frequent epidemic diseases were not isolated, but herded into the same ward with the other patients. The maternity ward, in charge of midwives, was separate, but this was for reasons of modesty — not to protect the mother and child from contagion. For nearly ten centuries the Hôtel-Dieu was the only public hospital in Paris where the poor could get medical attention, such as it was.

The companion surgeons were resident students who worked under visiting master surgeons. They dressed wounds, assisted with operations, and did what little they could to comfort the sick and the dying. Only desperately ill patients who had no other place to go were admitted, and many of them did not recover. In fact, all hospitals in those days were actually disease-breeders.

But there was perhaps no better place for an earnest student to gain experience with every sort of disease. Paré himself said later that he considered his three years in the Hôtel-Dieu more valuable than a course in surgery. Undoubtedly it also gave him a splendid chance to learn anatomy, since both autopsies and dissections were performed in the basement of the hospital. Eager as he was to learn, he never once forgot that he was treating fellow creatures in agony, or became indifferent to their suffering.

When he left the hospital in 1536 Paré had acquired a great deal of practical knowledge, and right away, in the new war between Francis I of France and Charles V of Germany, he began his career as an army surgeon. Although he had not taken his barber-surgeon examination, he was appointed personal surgeon to Marshall de Montejan, a colonel in the

French infantry. He was not officially in the army, but his duties allowed him time to help care for the wounded.

Since there was no organized military medical service, or even any regular provisions for treating casualties, a surgeon following the army sold his services as any itinerant doctor did. The patient paid what he could — usually a chicken, pig, or cask of wine looted from the countryside.

Military affairs were of little interest to Paré; he was first and always a doctor whose job was to heal the sick and wounded. During the opening campaign when the army crossed the Alps, his first case was an officer who had been shot in the ankle. Paré dressed the wound and nursed his patient back to health. Later he wrote, *"Je le pensait, Dieu le guerit."* (I tended him, but God cured him.) The same humble phrase is repeated many times in the writings of this unassuming, deeply religious man.

It was in this campaign that the young surgeon made his first important discovery — that the accepted methods of healing were not infallible. Many of the wounds he was called upon to treat were from shots made at such close range that there were powder burns. These were thought to be "poisoned with gunpowder," and to clean the wounds of the poison the surgeon poured boiling-hot oil of elderbush into them. The wounded men submitted to this agony in order to escape, as they hoped, death from poisoning.

This method of treatment had been taught by Giovanni de Vigo, surgeon to the Pope, and though Paré could hardly bear inflicting such pain, he used the boiling oil as the only possible course. But when the French stormed the castle of Villaine there were so many wounded that Paré ran out of elder oil. In desperation he had to think of a substitute. "I was constrained to apply in its place a concoction made of yolks of eggs, oil of roses, and turpentine. That night I could not sleep at my ease, fearing that by lack of cauterization I would find the wounded upon whom I had not used the said oil dead from the poison."

Early the next morning he hurried to his patients. Those who had been treated with boiling oil were feverish and contorted with pain, their wounds badly swollen. But those he had treated with his own concoction felt little pain, their wounds were not inflamed or swollen, and they had slept throughout the night! From this chance discovery, Paré learned that de Vigo's teaching was wrong. "Then I determined never again to burn thus so cruelly the poor men wounded by arquebuses."

He never did. But he believed that his emergency remedy could be improved upon. In 1537, while in Turin with the army, he met a surgeon who told him that he had a secret salve for dressing gunshot wounds. For two years he dogged this surgeon until finally by guile and gifts he was persuaded to confide his secret. And what a witch-brew it was! Newborn puppies boiled in oil of lilies, then mashed with earthworms and stirred in turpentine and white wine! The fact that Paré used this fantastic "remedy" for many years is an indication of the lack of knowledge that existed in the era in which he lived.

Because of his skill and devotion, soldiers going into battle gained confidence if Paré was with the troops, and on every hand the wounded on the battlefield cried for his help. Presently Montejan himself fell sick with a liver disorder that ultimately caused his death, and sent for a distinguished physician from Milan. Seeing a great opportunity to learn, Paré worked eagerly beside the famous doctor, who was so impressed by the younger man's skill that he told Montejan:

"You have a surgeon youthful in age, but old in knowledge and experience; regard him well, for he will serve you well and bring you honor." When he recorded this story, Paré wrote: "But the good man did not know that I had lived three years at the Hôtel-Dieu de Paris, to heal the sick there."

After more than two years with the army, Paré returned to Paris determined to be admitted as a barber-surgeon. In 1541, on the second try, he passed the examinations and became a Surgeon of the Short Robe. The same year he married and settled on the left bank of the Seine in the parish of St. André des Arts, where his practice flourished. His wife had brought him a small dowry, and this, with his medical fees, enabled him to buy several houses which he rented out, thus adding to his income.

But Paré was not satisfied with a merely remunerative practice. He wanted to reform the prevailing treatment of wounds, and to convince the medical world that cautery was wrong. Sylvius, Professor of Medicine at the university, heard of the young surgeon's new treatment, and invited him to dine. It may seem strange that Sylvius, the rigid follower of Galen, who had fought Vesalius and the school of younger anatomists, should be at all impressed with Paré. But in Galen's time there had been no gunpowder, so there was nothing in his books about pouring hot oil into gunshot wounds. Thus the sacrosanct image of Galen did not prevent Sylvius from accepting this new idea. In fact, he urged the young man to write about his method, though he was unversed in Latin and therefore not accepted as a man of learning.

Paré followed this advice, and set to work on his book, meanwhile buttonholing every colleague to talk about his theory. But since he did not speak the official language of the almighty medical faculty, his word carried little authority. Cautery with boiling-hot oil continued.

The little book, describing in every-day language the new method of treating gunshot wounds, came off the press in 1545. Paré's first literary venture was a success. His book was reissued several times to include new material. Today it is a medical classic. Taking heart from this warm reception of his book, the modest barber-surgeon began to write on other subjects.

He continued to study anatomy, which he had from the first recognized as essential to good surgery. Whether in the basement of the Hôtel-Dieu or on the battlefield, he undertook dissection at every opportunity. After the publication of his book, he dissected many cadavers by himself and at times as prosector for Sylvius, leaving one side of the specimen intact as a guide for surgery. He now wrote a small book on anatomy, again in French. Printed in 1549, it provided barber-surgeons with valuable anatomical information.

Only twice during this relatively peaceful period did Paré return briefly to field surgery, but in 1552 war broke out again and he resumed military service, following the armies for many years. Serving under four successive kings, his fame as a surgeon became a legend, and the wounded took comfort from his mere presence on the field. In an account of his travels, he wrote about the siege of Metz: ". . . and they received me with great joy, doing the honor of embracing me, and saying that I was welcome, adding that they had no more fear of dying, if they should happen to be wounded."

Always tender toward humans who were suffering, he

Ambroise Paré

was as ready to treat a wounded enemy as one of his own camp. Once, when taken prisoner, he worked with such devotion tending the sick, and curing one of the officers of a chronic leg sore, that he was granted his freedom.

During the campaign of 1552, Paré made his most important contribution to surgery. Many leg and arm wounds caused by short-range guns could not be cured except by amputation of the limb. But the risk to life was so great and the pain so frightful that even essential operations were often avoided. When it was done, a red-hot iron was applied to the stump after the amputation, to stop the flow of blood. This destroyed flesh, and the burned tissue poisoned the wound. If the patient survived this damage with its resultant fever, after a few days the escharred scab often fell off, re-exposing the open blood vessels, and the excruciating cautery would have to be repeated.

Paré had been thinking about a different way to control hemorrhage and had, in fact, discussed his idea with other surgeons. An opportunity to experiment came when he had to amputate a badly smashed leg. He used a forceps, similar to the modern hemostat, to pinch off the blood vessels which he then tied immediately after the amputation. This tying of blood vessels, or ligaturing, was not new; Paré knew that Galen used ligatures, and others from time to time had revived the procedure. But in his day it had fallen into disuse, and when he introduced it in amputations, there was the usual hue and cry against the innovation.

In 1585, thirty-three years after his first successful ligature experiment, Paré was still impelled to write in his *Apology:* "Truly I had not put my hand to the pen to write in such a manner, were it not that some have impudently taxed and insulted me, and disgraced me, more by particular hate . . . concerning my manner of tying the veins and arteries." Then, describing his chief assailant as "an aged man, who calls himself a wise doctor" who should "put off and drive out from him all envy and rancor conceived against his neighbor," he goes on "to prove to him by authority, reason, and experience, that the said veins and arteries should be tied." As his authorities he cited Hippocrates, Galen,

Avicenna, Guy de Chauliac, Celsus, and Vesalius. The last-named, in his *Surgery* "directs that the vessels be tied" if there is a flow of blood. However, Paré had to defend the practice which he had introduced in amputations.

When Paré returned to Paris he was still a lowly barber-surgeon whose lack of formal education would ordinarily have prevented his taking the examinations for master surgeon. But his fame and popularity brought him to the attention of Henry II, and he was appointed surgeon to the King. Though the diehards raved, the College of Saint Côme could no longer ignore his accomplishments, and going through the formality of "examining" him, they granted him the degree. At long last he was a Surgeon of the Long Robe.

Unlike Paracelsus and Vesalius, Paré did not come to grips with Galen in matters of theory, nor did he challenge the ancients in any of his writings. But like them a keen observer and skillful practitioner, he learned to believe only what he saw, and if this did not jibe with accepted theory, he bypassed the theory. Also like Paracelsus, he was willing and eager to learn from anyone, however humble.

One day during a military campaign a kitchen boy fell into a cauldron of boiling oil. Paré was called to dress the wounds, and went to the apothecary for some cooling preparation in common use for burns. Instead, as he relates, "there was present by chance a certain old country woman, who hearing that I desired medicines for a burn, persuaded me at the first dressing that I should lay on raw onions mashed with salt; for so I should hinder the breaking out of blisters."

Experimenting with this folk remedy, Paré found the next day that those parts of the boy's body to which he had applied the onions were free of blisters, while the untreated parts were heavily blistered. He drew no conclusions from this one case, but remembered what he had seen, and waited.

Soon he was called to treat a guard whose face and hands were badly burned by an explosion of his powder flask. To one half of the injured man's face Paré applied the onion poultice, to the other half the usual cooling remedies. At the time of the second dressing he found the area under the onion poultice was free from blisters and raw, peeled spots, while the other side of the face showed both, ". . . whereby I gave credit to the medicine." But he still drew no conclusions, and like a modern scientist continued his experiment.

In the storm of battle many soldiers were burned, and Paré dared to treat some of them with raw chopped onion instead of the old remedies. Every time the comparison was in favor of the onions. Needing a theory to explain their effectiveness, he fell back on Galen's principle that "contraries are cured by contraries." He became quite entangled in this theory, because onions were "hot" and therefore not "contrary" to burns. Somehow he concluded that they were only "potentially hot" and that their moisture drew the heat from the wound. We can hardly blame Paré for his far-fetched explanation, since in our own day extracts from onions and similar plants are being studied for their anti-infective properties, and even now the chemical nature of these substances and how they act is not known.

The fact that Paré's burn remedy was used for more than a century is evidence that his books, which were translated into Latin, German, Italian, and other languages, were widely read and influential in changing medical practices.

Right up to his death at the age of eighty, Ambroise Paré was active as surgeon in the royal court, on the battlefield, and in private practice. Always experimenting and writing, he introduced the fitting of artificial limbs and eyes; he discovered a method of turning an infant during a difficult birth to aid in its delivery; and he advocated the use of a truss for hernias instead of what was then a risky operation. He wrote on medical as well as surgical subjects: the plague, smallpox, measles, tumors, the causes of monstrous human births. Everywhere he traveled he picked up valuable or curious bits of information, such as tying off the blood supply to prevent death from viper-bite.

One of his crusades was against the superstition that the bezoar stone, a resinous growth in goats, gazelles, and other animals, was an antidote to every known poison. In a spectacular manner and at a time when murder by poison was common, Paré destroyed the myth of the bezoar stone as a universal antidote. A criminal condemned to hang for a theft volunteered for the experiment. It was agreed that if the antidote worked, he would be set free. But when he was given the poison and the "antidote" he died in misery, crying that it would have been better to die on the gallows. Paré performed an autopsy, which showed convincingly that the poison was the cause of death, and forever laid to rest the bezoar stone superstition.

To the young doctors Paré preached: Do your best for the good of the patient without regard to financial reward; treat even when it seems hopeless, for nature may cure when the physician is without hope. A true humanitarian, Paré introduced gentleness, compassion, and personal warmth into the care of the sick, teaching, as did Paracelsus, that love was the basis of the healing art.

Paracelsus, Vesalius, and Paré were all men of the Renaissance, opening up the modern era in medicine, anatomy, and surgery. Like the other two, Paré fought for the principle that experience, observation, and a knowledge of anatomy must supplant slavish adherence to the written word. His contribution to the medical arts earned him the name of Father of Modern Surgery.

Paré died in the very act of bringing comfort to the starved and dying during the Siege of Paris in 1590. He was buried in his parish church of Saint André des Arts at the foot of the nave under the tower.

In the words of one historian, he always "talked freely for peace and for the good of the people, which made him as much loved by the good as he was wished evil and hated by the wicked."

CHAPTER SEVEN

The Hunter Brothers

I: Successful William

We skip a century and cross the English Channel to find a new era in surgery that begins to be based on modern science.

The hero of this period, whom we track down to a farm in southeast Scotland, would have ridiculed the suggestion that he would some day leave his mark on the history of surgery. The notion that "Jockie" Hunter would ever amount to anything would have made the young man shake with derisive laughter. But nobody would have thought of suggesting anything so absurd!

"Jockie" was Mrs. Hunter's nickname for her tenth and youngest child — John, born in 1728. At the time of his birth the Hunter family was living at Long Calderwood, a farmstead seven miles from Glasgow. Late in life, Mr. Hunter had decided to give up his not-very-successful grain business in the nearby town of East Kilbride, retire to the soil, and become, like his ancestors, a "little laird" or a small landholder. This move gave him a certain standing in the parish, but it did not provide a more prosperous family life, for the grudging soil and miserable climate meant scanty crops.

By the time John came into the world, the oldest son,

James, was thirteen and William, the second son, ten. Three of the children had died in infancy, and four others were to succumb soon after they reached maturity — all from tuberculosis, a scourge that claimed a great number of victims in those days. The damp, piercingly cold climate was as bad for weak lungs as it was for the crops; people accepted death and funeral processions and the grinding poverty of life on the sour, rocky soil with the same sad resignation.

John was an unattractive, short, chunky child with a shock of carrot-colored hair that hung untidily over a broad brow and light gray eyes. Quarrelsome, stubborn, and surly, he fought with his schoolmates and was a trial to his teachers and a disappointment to his parents. His father, who married at the age of forty-four, was well along in age by the time the willful youngster was tearing noisily through the house, and was too ill and burdened with worries to take him in hand. The boy was overly indulged by his mother — after all, he was her youngest — and besides, John had developed a handy weapon that he didn't give up until long after childhood. He would kick and scream, for hours if necessary, to get his way.

No wonder the undisciplined boy disliked the drafty parish school which the Hunter children attended and where the schoolmaster ruled with an iron rod. John used every wile and trick, whenever he could, to dodge the classroom and escape the rigid and dull routine that other children accepted obediently. And he learned precious little when he did attend, for his mind was elsewhere.

It would be wrong to picture John as lazy, although he certainly appeared so to his distressed parents, who constantly compared him with the model pupils, James and William. At his age these boys had shown promise of taking up professional careers, but John was forever exploring the woods and fields and streams.

A dullard at books, he knew more about ants, birds, bees, tadpoles, and worms than anyone in the neighborhood. He never tired of watching them, and to learn more about what they were like he cut them open. What he could not find out by himself he tried to learn by questioning everyone: Why do leaves turn yellow and red in the autumn? Why do clouds take different shapes? What makes grass grow where it isn't planted? He would stop the farmhands at their work and ply them with questions: Why does milk dry up in the cow's udder when her calf is taken away? Why does a fierce bull become a docile ox after it is gelded? Not knowing the answers, nor even wanting to know, the farmers thought John a nuisance. And his parents were sure that no good could possibly come from this idle foolishness, which showed no signs of abating as he grew older.

Now for the time being we shall leave John to his nature study at Long Calderwood, and follow his brothers — especially William, who later did so much to shape John's career.

James was a handsome, likeable young man, clever with the paint brush and, as his portraits showed, possessing an artist's insight into character. He had been at the top of his class in the parish school. When he graduated, he decided to become a lawyer. At fourteen he was drawing up legal papers as an assistant in a government office, and from there went on to Glasgow to study law at the university. Needless to say, his father was pleased with the prospect of having a lawyer in the family; a landed proprietor often found himself in need of one, and legal advice was costly.

William also led his class and planned to enter the ministry. He had earned a scholarship of ten pounds a year, and enrolled in the University of Glasgow, a freshman at thirteen. The stilted curriculum of theology, philosophy, logic, and mathematics was not all that young William absorbed in his five college years. He came under the liberalizing influences that were spreading from England and the Continent, and from some of his fellow students he learned about the riches of literature and art. By the time he received his degree, he had given up the idea of becoming a minister, a decision that disappointed his father.

On his return home, an opportunity for a different career came in the offer of an apprenticeship to William Cullen, a young country doctor. Cullen was only eight years older than William, and had not yet obtained his medical degree. He had learned his doctoring as apprentice to a Glasgow physician, and had been a ship's surgeon and an assistant to an apothecary in London. He had also studied some anatomy at the University of Edinburgh Medical School, which was rapidly earning a world-wide reputation.

William jumped at the chance to study with a master who, besides his medical knowledge, had a broad cultural outlook. It is to Mr. Hunter's credit that he agreed to his son's change of profession, and became reconciled to having a doctor instead of a minister in the family.

For William, the next three years were "the happiest years of my life," and the master, equally pleased with his choice of apprentice, found his "whole conduct more strictly and steadily correct than that of any other young person I have ever known." William was well mannered, diligent, and beyond reproach in his behavior, a galling example to his rebellious younger brother John.

At the end of the third year the master had a proposal for his protegé: they would form a medical partnership. Cullen would take care of the general practice, William the surgical and obstetrical cases. First, since they both needed more training, Cullen would go to Glasgow for his medical degree, and William would get his experience in London under prominent teachers of surgery.

This ambitious scheme depended upon their getting help from Mr. Hunter. The aging and ailing man had already sold part of his holdings to give his sons a good education. But Cullen's praise of William's ability and scholarship conjured up the vision of a great doctor in the family, honoring the Hunter name. He agreed to shoulder the additional financial burden, on William's assurance that he would return home to set up his practice. So in the fall of 1740, at the age of twenty-two, William sailed for London.

The first day after he arrived in the capital, without even taking a glimpse at the sights of the great city, the small-town youth headed straight for William Smellie's apothecary shop. Mr. Smellie, a huge man of gusty spirit and infinite compassion, was making history in a field that had always belonged to old women: obstetrics, the undisputed province of the midwife. He broke into this jealously guarded domain with his revolutionary ideas about the different presentations of the baby during labor. Until then it was thought that the baby "stands on its feet" in the mother's womb, tumbling over on to its head a month or two before birth. But Mr. Smellie, with his measurements of skeleton pelvises and his compressible fetal dolls, proved that no such somersault takes place at any time during pregnancy.

For the first time anywhere, his little group of students was initiated into the precise mechanics of labor, learned the

William Smellie

different positions that the fetus assumes, and how to assist the mother. Based on his measurements of the baby's body and the mother's pelvis Smellie constructed forceps shaped to the curves of the pelvis and the baby's head, and taught his students how to use them to safely deliver the infant in a difficult birth.

William knew that he had come to the right man. He lived above the apothecary's shop for a year, learned everything he could from manipulating the toy fetuses in the pelvises of skeletons, and accompanied him to the bedside of mothers in labor. Smellie charged the poor nothing, asking, in lieu of payment, permission to bring along his students for instruction.

Like Cullen, Smellie took William under his wing, guiding him in his anatomy education and giving him access to the best teachers in London. But William was ambitious and wanted to rise fast. He had struck up a professional friendship with Dr. James Douglas, an eminent obstetrician and anatomist, and as soon as he had learned all he thought that Smellie could teach him, he changed masters. What Smellie lacked in finesse and social polish, the doctor possessed in full measure. Besides, he was wealthy and had a marriageable daughter. Dr. Douglas offered young Hunter a position as his assistant and as tutor to his son who was something of a problem. William accepted and before long became engaged to the daughter, Martha Jane.

William's rapid climb up the social and professional ladder in his "darling London" ended the original plan for his return to Scotland, to the chagrin of Dr. Cullen and the great disappointment of his father. Mr. Hunter died three months after his son announced that he was not coming home. But shortly before he passed away, he wrote to William: ". . . if you can persuade me it is for your good, I will not be against it."

With the help of Dr. Douglas, William was accepted as a surgical student by St. George's Hospital, where his ability and fine presence were soon recognized. His brother James by this time had lost his interest in law, and because of William's success, he also decided to go to London and begin the study of medicine.

Leaving the older brothers in London, we return to Long Calderwood. John is now thirteen, and his mother has very wisely decided to take him out of school, only partly to save the expense.

———

James, as the oldest son, inherited the run-down estate. His going off to London, and Janet's marriage taking her to Glasgow, left Mrs. Hunter with only two daughters, "Dolly" and "Tibbie," to take care of the farm. The black sheep of the family could not be relied on for much help. Although "Jockie" had a way with the farm animals, his mind was still on nests and burrows in the woods. The glowing reports of William's achievements in London in contrast to his own ineptitude only infuriated the rebellious youth. To add to Mrs. Hunter's sorrow, Tibbie was coughing and bringing up blood — the dread signs which told her that one more of her children was being taken from her forever.

When John was seventeen, and still a ne'er-do-well, his mother apprenticed him to his brother-in-law, a cabinetmaker in Glasgow who had just married his sister Janet. John had displayed a certain dexterity with his hands; perhaps he could learn the trade. It might have turned out that way except that the brother-in-law was shiftless and neglected his shop for the company of his tavern friends. Before long his drinking led to his bankruptcy, and Janet died before she had been married a year.

John came back to the farm, still without a useful occupation. Trouble followed upon trouble for the Hunters. Tuberculous "Tibbie" breathed her last on the farm. In London Dr. Douglas, in whose home William was living, suddenly died. Mrs. Douglas, carrying out the dying wish of her husband, sent William to study in Paris. By the time he returned to London, in 1744, Martha Jane Douglas, whom he was planning to marry, was dead. Although William had never been overly loving or gay, his fiancée's death was a great shock. No one ever took her place in his heart and William remained a bachelor.

The family sorrows mounted. Jamie, who showed great promise in his newly chosen calling and who William said was the cleverest in the family, developed the night sweats, fever, and emaciation that spelled tuberculosis. No longer able to work, he took the long, winding way back to Scotland where he died three years later.

After all these tragedies, John, at twenty, saw only one way out of a miserable existence on the farm. He wrote to William. Could he join him in his work? If not, he would go into the army.

While William's first devotion was to his work — he had just opened a private anatomy school in his home — he also had a strong sense of duty. With James's death, he was the head of his family. Perhaps by taking on the responsibility of his unsuccessful young brother, he could pay off a debt to his parents whose sacrifices had made his success possible. Besides, John's letter came just when he needed an assistant. By all means, he answered, John should come. And so he did, riding horseback all the way to London.

If the uncouth and belligerent country bumpkin had had any regard for fashionable society and correct manners he would have been awed by his older brother's gentlemanly appearance, restrained manner, and cool suavity. William was slender, handsome, poised and above all urbane; he had long ago shed the rough-hewn look of a man brought up on a farm. But John had little use for the social assets that William had deliberately cultivated — soft-spoken, polite language and the polish of a Londoner — and no more thought of imitating his brother than of covering his coarse, rusty hair with a powdered wig.

Luckily, and with good sense, William didn't try to reform his graceless brother. He was in need of a helper, and John seemed eager to get to the anatomy room.

Two years earlier William had advertised a course in the "Art of Dissecting" with a cadaver for each student and instruction in surgery. Students flocked to his class and he took a house in Covent Garden, where he set up a dissecting room with space for about twenty.

With little preparation, John applied the scalpel, folding back the skin, then the fat and fibrous tissue, to expose nerves, veins, and the underlying muscles. William was delighted with his dissection of an arm, and led him quickly to the next step. He gave him another arm in which the arteries were injected with a colored wax to make them stand out distinctly. This was an innovation William had brought back with him from the Continent. John was an apt pupil, for this work was much like what had engrossed him from the time he had cut up the first wild animal.

At last the floundering young man had found the kind of work he liked, and from then on he progressed rapidly in exploring the intricacies of the human body. Though he had loathed book learning, he was fascinated by what he was now learning with eye, hand, and knife.

Outside the class the brothers went their separate ways. The untutored, unkempt younger brother could hardly fit into William's social circle, nor did he want to. He found companionship more to his liking among the noisy revellers in the taverns and gambling dens; card games, dice, roulette, and cockfights were the attractions for John. He preferred to spend his time that way, rather than join his brother at the nearby Drury Lane Theatre, where David Garrick was winning immortality in the plays of Shakespeare.

William must have decided to leave things as they were, for John was a great help to him. He was not only skillful at dissection, doing William proud, but his preference for low life was an asset. The ruffians with whom John had an easy familiarity proved indispensable to the success of the school, for among them were the shady characters who traded in corpses.

Human dissection in private anatomy schools such as William's was legal, yet there was no legal way of obtaining cadavers. The bodies of executed criminals were available, but if not secretly sold by the executioners or spirited away by the professional traffickers in this commodity they were sent to the universities and Barber-Surgeons' Guild. The private schools had to procure corpses on the "black market." This led to the lucrative business of "body snatching."

Under cover of darkness in the early winter evening, before the cemetery watchmen arrived and the police began their nightly rounds, a group known as "sack-'em-up men" would repair to some fresh grave. The still-loose sod was easily lifted and laid aside; a wooden shovel was used to avoid the noise of striking a stone with a metal tool. The coffin lid was forced open and the body pulled out and divested of its shroud, which was left in the grave. While one man carefully replaced the soft earth in the grave, the others sacked the body and lifted it over the cemetery wall. A man carrying a sack when people were still on the street created no suspicion.

There was a great demand for cadavers, especially by the better schools that provided one for each student, and because of the risks involved in this illegal trade, the "body snatchers" commanded high prices. Some worked on a retainer basis, undertaking to deliver a steady supply of corpses during the winter session. To strengthen their hold on the school owner they exacted an additional sum as "protection" money. The "sack-'em-up men" were of course recruited from the dregs of London. They were organized into gangs, fought each other for the trade, extorted, bribed, blackmailed, and prevented students, by any foul means at their command, from obtaining their own cadavers from legal sources.

At one time William's school was so popular that he had about a hundred students in the course, and needed at least that many corpses during the year. He gladly turned over to John the business of negotiating with these underworld gangs. John spoke their language, and made arrangements over a mug of ale in some tavern. They even liked Jock Hunter because he didn't act as their superior; he was thus assured a choice of specimens needed for a particular purpose. For instance, since William was interested in obstetrics, John was able to procure for dissection the bodies of women who died in pregnancy. Such material was rarely available to others.

Courses ended in the spring, because there was no way to keep the cadavers from deterioration in hot weather. William usually went off to the country then, but in 1749 he was called back to Scotland by the news of their mother's failing health. John, anxious not to interrupt his studies, remained in London. William had arranged for him to study at the Chelsea Hospital under the famous surgeon William Cheselden.

This was indeed a rare opportunity for John. Dr. Cheselden was especially known for his remarkable skill in cutting for bladder stones. He had developed such an ingenious technique that he was reputed to recover the stone in a few minutes, timed by an assistant holding a watch. Without the benefit of anesthesia, such record speed was very important: at least the patient would not die from the pain. Cheselden had lost only six patients in his first hundred operations, a record that brought him patients from all over Europe.

Cheselden's skill was not limited to lithotomies. He also performed delicate operations on the eye, being the first to make an artificial pupil in a patient with a cataract. Under this famous master John received his first lessons in surgery.

When the fall session opened in his brother's school, John had become so proficient in dissection that William made him a full-fledged instructor in anatomy. The next summer he returned to the hospital to continue his work under Cheselden. The third year the old master died, and William arranged another opportunity for exceptional training, this time under Percival Pott, a leading surgeon at St. Bartholomew's Hospital.

Pott's name has been perpetuated in four diseases that he described: a tumor of the scalp; a fracture of the leg; gangrene in the legs of the aged; and "soot-wart," a form of cancer in chimney sweeps. From Pott, John Hunter learned to appreciate a great principle in surgery — the natural healing powers of the tissues. In a day when the application of almost any medicament was likely to introduce infection into the wound, dependence on cleanliness and simple bandaging was the better part of surgical wisdom.

After nearly four years in London, John had to interrupt his hard work for a short time. Mrs. Hunter had died of a stomach ailment and John went to Scotland to arrange for the care of the farm, bringing his only sister back to London. Thus Dorothea ("Dolly") kept house for William with a motherly eye on both brothers.

John now found opportunities to do research in William's

school. In his first anatomical experiment he injected mercury into the tube *vas deferens*, leading from the testis; this led to his discovery of the continuity of the duct with the long, coiled part (epididymis) and the seminiferous tubules. When the testis was laid open, its substance was filled throughout with the mercury he had injected. With full acknowledgment of his brother's work, William demonstrated the preparation in his lectures.

Bitten by the research bug, John went on with other projects in which William participated. A major discovery of the Hunters was the charting of the "minor" circulation — the lymphatic system. Working on and off for some seven years, John traced these delicate vessels and showed that they carry excess food and wastes from the tissues to one of the large veins in the chest, and thus into the blood. Until this demonstration took place, it had been thought that the flow was the other way — out of the blood and into the lymphatics.

Other investigations followed from the dissecting room of the Hunter Anatomy School. On some of these the brothers worked separately: William, interested in obstetrics, traced the fetal circulation and John, the complicated nerve pathways, concerned with smell.

During these early years of their combined enterprise, William reported their discoveries for both, always giving John his full measure of credit. It had to be so, because the younger brother woefully lacked the training for writing or lecturing. He wrote very badly, and his grammar and spelling were appalling. Even more than writing, he dreaded the prospect of lecturing or presenting his work in public. Only in the dissecting room did he feel at home, working round the clock even during the summer when the stench of the ill-preserved specimens drove all others from the room.

Never having learned Latin, he lacked the first requirement of the Corporation of Surgeons to practice surgery in London, or even to enter the long apprenticeship required for a license. But this did not deter John Hunter, and like many others he ignored the organized surgeons, practicing surgery for years without a license. As early as 1752, he cured a patient with a stricture of the urethra, devising a special set of instruments and tubes for the operation. This was two years before he entered St. George's Hospital as a student in surgery. He must have distinguished himself there because as soon as the resident (house surgeon) had completed his required term John was appointed to replace him, over the heads of students who enjoyed seniority.

The house surgeon, who paid for his own room and board in exchange for the privilege of invaluable experience, was in charge of the surgical wards during most of the night and at other times when the staff surgeons were not on hand. Despite his meager training, of which he was all too aware, the unspeakable suffering all around him impelled John to increase his knowledge of healing. He longed to give more than the comfort of a fresh dressing, a soothing poultice, or the relief of pain with laudanum.

His responsibilities included the meeting of many emergencies. He had to stop hemorrhages, apply sutures where necessary, immobilize broken limbs, and wash open wounds with warm wine. Indefatigable John, intent on every patient's need, worked with the same absorption as in the dissecting room. For he was sure that surgery, medicine, and anatomy were indissolubly tied together and that experimentation advanced all three. In his scant free time he studied the blood, juggling air-pumps, stop-cocks, tubes, and bellows to discover how it takes in and releases oxygen.

Portrait of William Hunter (1718–1783) when he was about 35

John would have continued at St. George's Hospital, but William still hoped that his uneducated brother could profit from exposure to some intellectual influences. In the fall of 1755 he made arrangements for him to go to Oxford, and John, unwilling, but grateful for all William had done for him, went up to the great university. After two months he was back, protesting that they wanted to make an old woman of him, "stuffing" him with Latin. "But these schemes I cracked like so many vermin," he declared.

He returned to the flourishing anatomy school whose reputation grew as William's practice of obstetrics prospered. Its fame spread, even overseas to the American colonies. Two leading Philadelphia physicians — William Shippen and John Morgan — came to study with the Hunters, and a third — Benjamin Rush — considered his medical education in Edinburgh incomplete without a visit to the Hunter school in London.

William would have liked to give over part of his lecture classes to John, but the idea of addressing students from a platform threw the younger brother into a panic.

In 1759 John contracted pneumonia and, after recovering, was left with pains in the chest. He was then thirty-one, and the eleven years he had spent almost without interruption in the foul atmosphere of the hospitals and the dissecting room had taken their toll. To recover his health he needed a change. It came in the form of a commission in the army as staff surgeon, arranged through William's intervention with the Inspector General of Hospitals. This was during the Seven Years' War in which England and Prussia were allies against France, Austria, and Russia. John sailed with the fleet for Belle Isle, off the northwest coast of France.

The battle over, with a very costly victory for England, the British occupied the island and John got to work attending the sick and the wounded. Here he had an opportunity to prove, in the treatment of gunshot wounds, what he had learned from Pott's principle of uncomplicated treatment: reliance on the curative powers of nature. It had been the practice for over a century to remove the imbedded bullet from the flesh. This meant enlarging the wound, leading to more hemorrhage, greater pain and shock, and as we know today, an increased risk of infection.

"It is contrary to all rules of surgery founded on our

knowledge of the animal economy to enlarge wounds simply as wounds. No wound, let it be ever so small, should be made larger," John wrote many years later. He was able to prove his point by obtaining recoveries while leaving the bullet in, extracting it only when unavoidable. His defiance of the century-old practice of enlarging the wound didn't make him popular with the other surgeons. And he had little regard for them, for he wrote William: "My fellow Creatures of the Hospital are a damn'd disagreeable set. The two Heads are as unfit for employment, as the devil was to reign in Heaven."

Despite his arduous duties as army surgeon, John found time to indulge his childhood interest in nature. At low tide he spent hours collecting a variety of sea life — squid, starfish, jellyfish, and eels. Back in his quarters he dissected, bottled, and preserved hundreds of specimens. He was the first to make the interesting discovery that, like other fish, eels produce eggs. This he demonstrated by tracing the passages to the egg-forming structures. His interest in hibernation in later years may have started with the observation of lizards he caught on the island. He found that worms and bits of meat he placed in the lizard's throat in winter remained until spring, unaltered along the digestive canal. In these animals he also noticed the process of regeneration of the tails after repeated cutting.

The next expedition was to Portugal, where he was disappointed at being cheated out of a promotion. But he endured the slight, and the discomfort of life in base hospitals, since he had the opportunity to study the hearing of fish and the geology of the area around Lisbon.

On the signing of the peace in 1763, he returned to England on a retirement pay of five shillings a week. With him he brought his animal and rock specimens, the beginnings of what was to become one of the most fascinating collections ever made by a scientist.

From then on he was on his own, for William in the meantime had moved further up the ladder, becoming physician-extraordinary to Queen Charlotte, the first man ever to attend the Queen of England during labor. John's position in the school had been taken by a substitute whom William was keeping on, and a certain coolness developed between the brothers. John had no medical degree, and with William's influence withdrawn, no connections to secure him a hospital position or to help him set up in practice. Despite the poor prospects for the immediate future, it is possible that John was glad to be out of his big brother's shadow.

II: John—Surgeon Scientist

At the age of thirty-five John Hunter opened a modest office in Golden Square, a quiet residential part of London. He would have liked an anatomy school of his own, but was hardly in a position to undertake the expense, and still less was he able to compete with the established schools. While waiting for patients, and to supplement his meager pension, he accepted an offer that must have shocked not only his genteel brother but all self-respecting physicians of the time. The Spences, a father-and-son dental team, were looking for a surgical consultant — a fantastic idea for those days. For what was lower in quackery than a tooth-puller? But John Hunter, completely free of pretensions, accepted the job for three mornings a week. Events proved that a true scientist can break ground no matter where he plows.

In the five years he worked with the Spences, John made

enormous contributions to the field of dentistry, embodying his findings in a two-volume work, *Natural History of the Teeth*. He examined the teeth of nearly every animal that grows them, whether insect or lobster, finding them in the gullets of the earthworm or in the stomach of a mollusk. He studied the changes in human teeth from infancy to old age, and made a collection of nearly 600 specimens. He explained the intricate action of the muscles of mastication in bringing the jaws together in perfect occlusion of the upper and lower teeth.

He recognized that teeth which grow crooked interfere with the growth of and damage the adjoining teeth. He proposed ways to correct this by removing teeth that encroached on others or straightening them with braces not unlike those used today.

He suggested that the bony part under the enamel of the teeth was living tissue deriving its nutrition from blood vessels. He even tried to transplant teeth, hoping to make them grow into the socket tissues of the host. In this he failed, although for a while Hunter's followers tried to adopt the idea.

Before going off to war, John had made plans to start a menagerie for the study of all kinds of animals. He had leased two acres in Earl's Court in the village of Kensington where he proposed to build a house for his collection. Ill health had caused him to postpone the project, but now established in his modest practice, he carried out his plans, living in town and retiring to Earl's Court as often as he could.

The design of the house was as unique as the idea of the menagerie was unorthodox. Over the door hung the head of a crocodile with gaping jaws. Four life-size statues of lions, two rearing and two crouching, were set on each side of the building. Back of the house was a den where real lions and leopards were chained. Over the den there was a mound of earth, topped with piles of seashells, in the shape of a little fort on which was mounted a small gun.

The strangest sight was the barnyard. Here all kinds of domestic and wild animals roamed in confusion. Rare birds and serpents, ostriches, geese, and pheasants mingled with buffalos and deer. Fowl with human teeth grafted on the combs, hens with rooster's feathers, goats and dogs were all there for some type of experiment. In a small fishpond Hunter bred eels, leeches, carp, and river mussels. Hedgehogs and other hibernating animals were kept in burrows to yield their secrets of winter sleep. No specimen was too bizarre a subject for the surgeon-scientist to scrutinize. There were goose eggs for the study of embryology, pond water for fresh-water life, the skeleton of a giant dancing bear contracted for with a traveling gypsy when it was still alive.

He frequented the pet shops, looking for strange creatures, and begged zoo keepers and members of expeditions for any rare beasts they might encounter. Dead animals were useful, too. Certain parts he pickled in jars, others he dried. The rest were boiled down in a copper vat and the skeletons preserved.

John Hunter's collection was not the idle freak his bewildered neighbors considered it. Everything had a purpose. Whether he studied the air-sacs of birds, the electric organs of fish, the skeletons of whales and sea-cows, or the development of the ear membranes in the cow, deer, or hare, his interest was in the logical connection between similar structures in related species. Also he believed that in the early stages of their development, highly evolved animals exhibited features resembling those of simpler ones.

In the most roundabout way, an animal experiment sometimes led him to a new principle in human surgery. Once while studying the growth of antlers in deer, Hunter found that if he tied off the artery to the head on one side the antler became cold, but in a few weeks the circulation was completely restored. Autopsy showed that the blood had been shunted through other blood vessels.

Many years later he applied this observation to a patient with a clot inside a large pocket of a stretched and bulging artery in the knee. The customary treatment was to tie the vessel above and below the clot, and then scoop the clot out of the bulging pocket (aneurysm). The procedure was fatal so often that amputation was considered safer. Hunter recalled the experiment with the deer's antler. He tied the large artery in the triangular space (now called Hunter's canal) between three muscles above the knee, shutting off that branch of the circulation. Within six weeks the patient was well, his leg having been nourished by the blood shunted from neighboring connecting vessels. Since then this procedure for treating aneurysm has saved many a limb as well as life.

Hunter's work was beginning to receive professional recognition. His *Natural History of the Teeth* sold a thousand copies. In 1767, he was elected a Fellow of the Royal Society, an honor he especially relished because it was awarded to him before it was given to his already famous brother. Soon afterwards he became a member of the Corporation of Surgeons, and finally he received the appointment he coveted on the surgical staff of St. George's Hospital.

John's experience in the expeditionary forces had made him no friends among the army surgeons except for one older man, Robert Boyne Home, a Scot living in London. Mr.

Home asked John to visit him and his family when the campaign was over. Following the surrender of Belle Isle, Mr. Home returned to England and went into private practice.

Some time after John settled in Garden Square, he thought of looking up his old friend. The Homes were a happy family of moderate means. There were four sons and three daughters, nearly all of whom distinguished themselves in some fashion. The oldest son was a painter. Another son was an administrator with the East India Company. Daughter Anne painted, composed music, played the harpsichord, and wrote poetry that has lived after her. *To a Nightingale,* and the lyric, *My Mother Bids Me Bind My Hair,* which Haydn set to music, were among her many works.

Anne was a tall, slender, golden-haired beauty, kindly, warm, and much sought after in London's social circles. To the amazement of her friends, when John, fourteen years older, short and heavyset, uncultured and scornful of the social amenities, fell in love with her and asked for her hand in marriage, she consented. Beneath that unattractive exterior Anne recognized a fine human being and a great man passionately devoted to a life of investigating the unknown.

The Homes may have hoped for a more prosperous union for their attractive daughter, but they accepted John with good grace. Not so William. Unmarried himself, he was not sympathetic to the idea of marriage for his brother, and certainly not to a woman who brought him no dowry. In any event, John could not marry immediately, even though he was nearly forty. While he told Anne quite truthfully that he was not yet able to support a family on his income, there was another reason that he kept to himself.

In order to test a theory about venereal disease, he had deliberately infected himself with pus taken from one of his

patients. He promptly developed the disease with all its devas-
tating symptoms, which he watched with the same objectivity
with which he approached problems in animals and cadavers.
Rubbing mercury into his sores, he finally rid himself of the
surface symptoms. After three years, during which Anne
waited patiently, he decided that he was cured and ready to
marry.

One Sunday morning in the summer of 1771, the quiet
ceremony, witnessed by Anne's parents and a few intimate
friends, took place in St. James's Church in Piccadilly. William
was invited but did not attend. Captain James Cook, just returned from a voyage, was one of the wedding guests, and
presented John with a gift of plants and animals he had
brought back from the South Seas.

John took his bride to Earl's Court for a two-day honeymoon spent amid his strange beasts and specimen jars. This
was characteristic of the eccentric surgeon, but his charming
and loving wife never then or later complained of her lot.

Their town home in Jermyn Street, which he took over
when William moved to more pretentious quarters, over-
flowed with fossils, skeletons, double-headed monsters, and
every imaginable anatomical specimen. A stuffed giraffe resting on its knees greeted callers in the entrance hall.

Cheerfully, and with genuine grace, Anne maintained an
elegant household, and the élite and distinguished of London
came for the brilliant conversation, poetry readings, music,
and entertainment provided by the charming hostess. Some
may have been intrigued by the curious combination of refine-
ment and taste with the raw and unsavory sights and smells of
the Hunter home. It is said that one woman, in her curiosity
to see it, called at the house with the excuse that she wished
to be bled.

One evening when John returned late after a hard day's work, he unexpectedly found his drawing-room filled with "musical professors, connoisseurs, and other idlers, whom Mrs. Hunter had assembled." Greatly irritated, he walked straight into the room and told the astonished guests: "I knew nothing of this kick-up, and I ought to have been informed of it beforehand; but as I am now returned home to study, I hope the present company will retire." The visitors promptly exited.

But not all the visitors came at Anne's invitation. John had his own small but devoted circle who called him "that dear man." His keen mind, stimulatingly novel ideas, and vast store of knowledge, as well as his hearty love of life and spicy wit, brought him many devotees. The explorers Captain Cook, Joseph Banks, and George Cartwright sought his company for what they could learn from his penetrating investigations.

His highly select house students, who later distinguished themselves in their own right, sat admiringly at his feet, overlooking his eccentricities and, in fact, finding him "extremely companionable. His wit, or more properly his archness, was always well directed," one commented. Another: "Mr. Hunter was a man of very considerable humour. His views of subjects in general were quick and peculiar, and when so disposed he could place them in very ludicrous points of view." And another: " . . . standing alone in this branch of science, [anatomy] and high in the public estimation, he had so much attention paid to him that no new animal was brought to this country which was not shown to him; . . . "

John's appointment to St. George's brought him a good income, and the enhanced prestige of this hospital connection increased his private practice. The appointment also carried with it the right to take on medical apprentices who served for five years, each paying several hundred pounds in fees.

These fees were divided equally among the four surgeons at
the hospital and became a bone of contention between him
and the other surgeons in the hospital: " . . . what galled them,"
his biographer writes, "was the crowd of pupils that entered
under him, not under them; the rush to go round the wards
with him, and his name in everybody's mouth, his rough jokes
at their expense, his outspoken contempt of their pathological
doctrines."

His attitude toward his colleagues, which created many
enemies for him, stemmed less from vanity than from impatience with their ignorance and smugness. Says Abernethy,
one of his pupils: "He felt irritated by the opposition he had
met with. . . . 'I know, I know,' said he, 'I am but a pigmy
in knowledge, yet I feel as a giant, when compared with these
men.' "

Characteristic of the way he selected his house pupils —
among whom were Dr. Philip Syng Physick of Philadelphia,
Henry Cline of London, and Edward Jenner of smallpox vac-
cine fame — was this interview with one applicant: "Well,
young gentleman, so you are come to town to be a surgeon.
And how long do you intend to stay?" "One year," the young
man replied. "Then, I'll tell you, that won't do. I've been here
a great many years, and yet I don't know the principles of the
art." On the other hand, when another said he was not attending the lectures, because he was not yet sufficiently advanced
to profit by them, Hunter told him: "That, Sir, is very compli-
mentary, but I will give you a perpetual ticket, and shall be
glad to see you whenever you will call."

He had no interest in money for the comfort it could buy
him. All he could spare of his earnings he put into his collection, and even went into debt for a rare animal or valued specimen. From 1772 on he made frequent use of Earl's Court,

sleeping there in the fall months and coming into town in the morning. Mrs. Hunter had to choose between the house in Jermyn Street, its rooms invaded by anatomical preparations, and the villa at Earl's Court, with its grounds full of strange or hostile animals.

Despite all his wife had to put up with, she not only took her lot cheerfully but gave him her abiding devotion, soothed his irritations, understood his self-denial, and appreciated his worth. And John loved his "Anny" with a quiet, unostentatious affection and deep pride in her accomplishments. Altogether their domestic life was a happy one. Of four children born to them during the first five years of their marriage, the first two died in infancy. Agnes and Jock — John Banks Hunter — they brought up into adulthood. "I am not anxious about my children but in their doing well in this world. I would rather make them feel one moral virtue, than read libraries of all the dead and living languages," John wrote to Dorothea's husband, Reverend James Baillie.

———

Beginning in 1773, John gave a yearly course of lectures three evenings a week throughout the winter months. The content was advertised as "Principles and Practice of Surgery, in which will be introduced so much of the Animal Oeconomy as may be necessary to illustrate the Principles of those Diseases which are the Object of Surgery." During the year he gave a hundred of these lectures at a fee of four guineas (about twenty dollars); a listener paid tenpence per lecture, while anyone working in the dissection room at Jermyn Street was admitted free.

Lecturing was always an unpleasant task to Hunter who had never lost his fear of addressing a class. He would brace himself each time by taking thirty drops of laudanum before facing the large audiences who came to hear his ideas on embryology, physiology, "animal chemistry," properties of matter, and the "life of the blood." The lectures took a great deal of his time and energy to prepare, since each was illustrated with materials from his unique museum, and he was continually revising and adding to his notes in the light of new observations. "You had better not write down that observation, for very likely I shall think differently next year," he would say to a prodigious note-taker. To one student who pointed out that he had just contradicted a statement of the year before, he replied: "Very likely I did: I hope I grow wiser every year."

In 1773 he had his first attack of angina, the result of heart damage from the disease he had deliberately given himself years earlier. He described his symptoms in these words: "As I was walking about the room, I cast my eyes on a looking-glass, and observed my countenance pale, my lips white, and I had the appearance of a dead man looking at himself. This alarmed me. I could feel no pulse in either arm. The pain still continuing, I began to think it very serious. I found myself at times not breathing; and being afraid of death soon taking place if I did not breathe, I produced a voluntary action of breathing, working my lungs by the power of my will. . . ."

These attacks recurred many times in later years, but he maintained the same back-breaking schedule, on four or five hours of sleep. Beginning every morning before six, he would dissect until nine, eat a brief breakfast, see patients until noon, and then make his hospital rounds. He dined sparingly at four, slept for an hour, and spent the evening preparing or delivering lectures. At midnight, after the family had gone to bed, the butler would bring him a lamp with a fresh wick, and he would continue to work until two or three in the morning.

When a friend warned him: "John, you are always at work!" he replied: "I am, and when I am dead, you will not soon meet with another John Hunter."

He never dropped one burden without picking up another. When the lectures were over, he opened his museum to visitors, demonstrating his preparations himself: in October for the profession, and in May for "noblemen and gentlemen who were in town only during the spring." He wrote papers, lectured before the Royal Society and other learned bodies, and performed innumerable autopsies at the hospitals. Always in search of animals and specimens for his collection, he wrote hundreds of letters to Edward Jenner, former pupil and kindred spirit in natural history, to explorers, and scientists all over the world, asking them to send him material.

For years he practically haunted the Irish giant, Byrne (born O'Brien) whose eight-foot skeleton he coveted. The poor man desperately tried to evade him, but every time Hunter managed to track him down. Byrne willed that when he died his body should be placed in a lead coffin, taken out to sea and sunk; at his death the body was placed under heavy guard. Hunter found out when the men on duty had gone off for a drink. He went to the tavern and bribed them with five hundred pounds which he had to borrow, and was able to arrange for the removal of the corpse in a hackney-coach. It was then transferred to his own carriage and taken to Earl's Court. He sectioned the body, removed the flesh by boiling in a huge vat, and reassembled the skeleton, which later hung in his study. In the portrait that Joshua Reynolds painted of Hunter, the dangling legs of the giant can be seen in the background.

By 1783, when his brother William died, John was un-

*The copper at Earl's
Court House in which
the body of Byrne
O'Brien, the famous
Irish Giant, was
boiled in 1783 by
John Hunter*

rivalled in anatomy, and when Potts too passed away, John
Hunter became the first surgeon of London. He had been appointed Surgeon Extraordinary to the King, and it was more
than he could do to take care of his enormous practice. Although the income from his patients amounted to more than
five thousand pounds a year, he was always in debt. It is estimated that his collection cost seventy thousand pounds, and
when it outgrew the space in Jermyn Street, he leased a large
house in Leicester Square that he could scarcely afford.

The expense of keeping the town and country establish-
ments was fabulous. A listing of the members of the household shows that he maintained some fifty people! In addition
to Mrs. Hunter, their two children, his brother-in-law, and

*Portrait of John Hunter by Sir Joshua Reynolds. The legs of
the giant can be seen in the background*

the five students, who paid for their keep, there were in the town house: a housekeeper, a doorkeeper, the man in charge of dissecting and lecture rooms, a secretary, and the caretaker of the museum. At Earl's Court there were coachman, footman, butler, cook, housemaid, seamstress for Mrs. Hunter, gardener, housekeeper, dairymaid, field man, gardener in charge of the greenhouse, and a woman to weed the garden and fetch the cows. There were always some outside workers: sawyer, carpenter, plumber, bricklayer, painter, glazier, blacksmith, or printer.

In his last years Hunter was almost constantly in pain, suffering from dizziness, lightheadedness, and sporadic loss of memory, but he drove himself to the end. Whether he was working with animals or patients — whom he treated with infinite care and gentleness — he never ceased trying to understand and to learn more about the organization of life and the causes of disease. Despite all the demands on his time and his heavy expenses, he treated the poor without charge. In his closing affectionate remarks at the end of each year's course, he urged the students to seek his advice free whenever they had a patient with a puzzling disease.

Even when close to death from illness and overwork, he planned further experiments, writing to a friend in Africa to send him ostrich eggs, a camel, cuckoos, a young lion, everything "respecting the bee tribe," chameleons, and any other beast or bird he could find.

On October 16, 1793, he rose as usual before dawn to do his daily dissecting. Working with his students later in the morning he interrupted the lesson, as was his habit, to relate an anecdote from his practice. Talking about children who feign illness to avoid school, he told them of the boy who "developed" a limp. He advised the parents to put the boy to bed, place a bunch of grapes on the other side of the room, and then peek through the keyhole. As soon as the boy thought he was alone, he leaped across the room without a sign of a limp.

Whistling a lively Scottish tune, his good spirits suddenly faded when he remembered that he had to attend a Board meeting at St. George's. The point at issue was the admission of two students from Scotland (their nationality being one count against them) who did not have a "certificate of their having been bred to the profession." Hunter, remembering his own early difficulties in obtaining a hospital connection, sympathized with them and intended to intercede, which he did.

While he was appealing to the Board, a couple of his opponents broke in with some insolent remarks. Such encounters always aroused his anger, and anger would bring on a violent chest pain. He used to say: "My life is in the hands of any rascal who chooses to annoy or tease me." This time Hunter stopped speaking, staggered out of the room, and fell unconscious. That afternoon he died. Everard Home, Anne's brother and Hunter's student, performed the autopsy which John always had insisted should be done on every man of science. It was found that John Hunter had died from an aneurysm of the aorta, a consequence of the disease with which he had infected himself in the pursuit of scientific knowledge.

He was buried after a simple ceremony, in a vault of Saint Martin's-in-the-Fields. The enmities he created by his independent spirit, advanced ideas, and impatience with traditional practices, were deep enough to prevent any official honors at the time of his death. It was not until 1859 that his body was moved to Westminster Abbey and with appropriate ceremonies laid to rest beside the tomb of Ben Jonson.

Thanks to the efforts of Lord Auckland, a friend of Hunter's, the government gave Anne a small pension. His collection went unsold for several years but was finally bought by the government and placed in the care of the Royal Society of Surgeons in London. It is on permanent exhibit for the benefit of future scientists.

The Hunterian Museum has been estimated to contain over 13,000 specimens, at least 500 different species of animals, all anatomized by Hunter, in addition to human pathological preparations, the skulls of people of all nationalities, stuffed animals, and fossils.

Among the specimens is the skeleton of the Irish Giant. In 1909, Harvey Cushing, the American brain surgeon, received permission to open the giant's skull. Evidence of a pituitary tumor established the cause of Byrne's tremendous size.

Without formal schooling, completely self-educated, John Hunter set the highest standards for the education of a surgeon. Coming into the profession when, in his own words, a surgeon was "a savage with a knife," he raised it to the level of an honorable calling. He was a highly distinguished practical surgeon, made vast contributions to comparative anatomy, and opened the field of pathological anatomy as a vital adjunct to surgery. His genius for discovering the orderly and systematic organization of living structures and their activities was an inspiration to a large number of students. But if his scientific method had influenced one man only — Edward Jenner — he would have earned an honored place among the great teachers of medicine.

Far ahead of his time, John Hunter's work in advancing surgery toward a scientific path has gained ever fuller recognition with each decade since his passing.

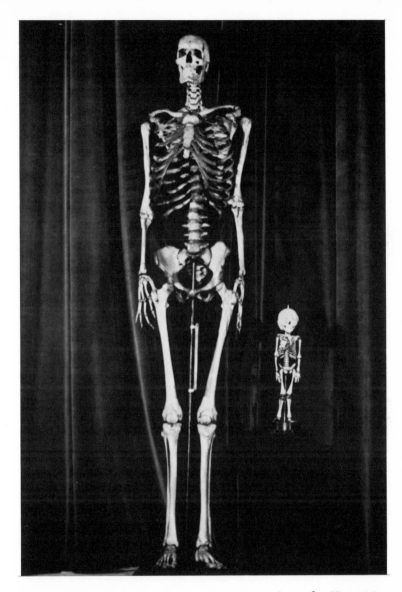

The skeletons of the Giant and the Dwarf in the Hunterian Museum

CHAPTER EIGHT

Surgery without Agony

Something over a century ago a new word was added to the language of surgery: *anesthesia.* It was coined by Oliver Wendell Holmes, the famous New England writer and physician, to designate a state of "insensibility" unknown until then. Wrote the good-humored Dr. Holmes to Dr. W. T. G. Morton of Boston: "Everybody wants to have a hand in a great discovery. All I will do is to give you a hint or two, as to names, or the name, to be applied to the state produced and the agent. The state should, I think, be called 'anesthesia.' This signifies insensibility. . . . The adjective will be 'anesthetic.' " And so it remains, a word that tells the story of man's conquest over pain in surgery.

Before the discovery of anesthetics, surgery was, of necessity, performed on struggling, agonized patients who had to be tied down by ropes or held by strong-armed assistants. The horrible shrieks of those under the knife subsided only when they were carried out prostrate, in shock from the pain, weakened and bruised by the ordeal. Many patients died simply from the pain and rough handling.

The search for pain-killers parallels the early story of

surgery itself, when progress was tortoise-paced. Opium, hemp, and the twisted root of the mandrake plant were known to the Egyptians, Greeks, and Babylonians. Wine was often mixed with some herbal to prepare an ancient soporific for the patient to drink before an operation. Or, "sleeping" sponges were soaked in a concoction of mandrake root or some other herb and applied to the nose of the patient. Made senseless by the poisonous potion, the patient was often aroused from his stunned sleep by the first entrance of the knife into his flesh. Since there was no way of knowing how much of the draught to administer, the patient sometimes died from an overdose. In fact the risk of death from these drugs often deterred surgeons from attempts at pain-killing, and in France a law was passed during the seventeenth century forbidding their use.

Paré, the gentlest of surgeons, applied pressure to the carotid artery (in the neck) to render his patient unconscious, and Baron Dupuytren, the most callous of surgeons, was known to throw a woman patient into a dead faint with some insult before applying the knife. Some tried freezing with snow the part under surgery. Toward the end of the eighteenth century Mesmerism, a form of hypnotic suggestion, was employed by those few who were adept at it.

The most humane surgeons were hopeless of sparing pain with any known drug or method. Paré and Hunter taught moderate use of the scalpel, resorting to surgery only when all other means were exhausted. And Cheselden was so unnerved by the thought of the suffering inflicted that he was known always to vomit before an operation.

Conscientious surgeons sought to improve their skill to the point where they could perform an operation in a few minutes. Naturally, the speediest operators were the most in de-

Alcohol fumes used as an anesthetic in a monastery hospital

mand. This meant that by the end of the eighteenth century surgery was at a standstill. No progress could be made if success depended only on speed. Only such operations as amputations, the removal of stones, or of superficial tumors could be done quickly. Surgery on internal organs was impossible, and would be until pain could be conquered.

Despair at ever finding a satisfactory pain-killer was so ingrained that when pain-killing chemicals became available their value in surgery went unrecognized for many years.

Humphry Davy, the son of a poor woodcarver, was born in Penzance, Cornwall in 1778. His early tastes were for translating the classics, writing verse, and telling fanciful stories. His father died in 1794 and the sixteen-year-old lad turned to science and became one of England's most versatile and brilliant scientists.

His probable intention to become a doctor led him to sign up as an assistant to a surgeon apothecary. But his wide reading in metaphysics, mathematics, and chemistry detoured him to another road. Thomas Beddoes, a Shropshire physician, had founded a Pneumatic Institute where he used various gases to treat asthma and other respiratory diseases. He put young Davy to work on his medicinal inhalants.

One day Davy inhaled some nitrous oxide (N_2O), a gas discovered some twenty years earlier by Joseph Priestley, the discoverer of oxygen. The young man found that it relieved the pain from his inflamed gums. Following up this observation in animals, he reported: "As nitrous oxide in its extensive operation appears capable of destroying physical pain, it may probably be used to advantage during surgical operations in which no great effusion of blood takes place."

Sir Humphry Davy

No one, including Davy himself, paid attention to this prophetic remark. His interest was in chemistry, in which he advanced rapidly. At the age of twenty-three, he was appointed assistant lecturer in chemistry, and director of the chemical laboratory in the new Royal Institution chartered by the King. His brilliant lectures attracted fashionable London. He possessed the great gift of explaining complicated ideas in simple, clear language and of embellishing his talks with ingenious figures of speech. Coleridge, the English poet, once said he attended Davy's lectures to increase his "stock of metaphors." Equally eloquent with the pen, Davy was selected as assistant editor of the *Journal of the Royal Institution.*

His researches in chemistry were rapidly productive. He isolated sodium, potassium, calcium, and barium and proved them to be separate elements. These achievements put him in the forefront of chemistry. His studies in electricity were equally remarkable, and Napoleon, though at war with England, awarded him a medal in 1808 for an experiment in galvanism. His own country knighted him in 1812, and in 1820 Sir Humphry became president of the Royal Society of England. To this day he is remembered for his invention of the safety lamp, still used to reduce the risk of explosions in mines.

Sir Humphry Davy himself said that his greatest discovery was Michael Faraday, whom he employed as his assistant and valet on a trip on the Continent. But Davy's discovery of the anesthetic properties of nitrous oxide or laughing gas went unnoticed for about half a century; he himself made no further study of the gas.

Curiously, this quality of the gas was rediscovered by professional entertainers and showmen. In the initial stages of inhalation it has an exciting effect, throwing the inhaler into fits of laughter and sending him into giddy spins. Trooping "lecturers" would demonstrate its effects in sideshows. Daring volunteers in the crowd tried it on themselves.

Samuel Colt, a young New Englander, seized upon these popular demonstrations as a way of financing the patenting of a revolver he had invented. Equipping himself with the paraphernalia for inhaling nitrous oxide, he advertised himself as Dr. Colt and presented his show on the town green. The willing inhalers in his audience amused the onlookers with their giggles and wild antics.

Even in the sleepy little town of Jefferson, Georgia young people had somehow gotten wind of the exhilarating effects of nitrous oxide. The innocent old-fashioned quilting parties, popular in those days, now became gatherings where the boys and girls danced and then ended the evening with a laughing-gas "frolic." The craze spread through the country.

Crawford Williamson Long, the town doctor, who was only twenty-seven, and his four still younger students, had seen itinerant lecturers demonstrate the marvels of chemistry and especially the intoxicating effects of nitrous oxide. The students had taken part in these inhalation parties.

One evening they asked Long to prepare some gas for them, for the town doctor was also the apothecary. Since he had neither the equipment for preparing it, nor the means to preserve the gas, he couldn't oblige them.

"But I have a medicine that I use to ease a hacking cough and to bring up phlegm," he told them.

This medicine, sulfuric ether, would be equally exhilarating; he had inhaled it himself, and it was as safe as nitrous oxide, he assured his students.

That evening everyone in the party took a whiff of ether, and all were well pleased with the effects. Thus Long started the ether frolics which "soon became quite fashionable in this country, and in fact extended from this place through several counties in this part of Georgia," Long related. He noticed that after inhaling the vapors the subjects staggered and reeled, often falling to the ground. But the bruises they suffered seemed to cause them no pain.

Ether, first called "sweet vitriol," was discovered in the

sixteenth century, yet despite the desperate search for pain-relievers, it had never been applied to surgery. Paracelsus, the nomadic doctor of that century, was "warm" in this hunt, when he wrote:

". . . it has associated with it such a sweetness that it is taken even by chickens, and they fall asleep from it for a while but awaken later without harm. On this sulfur no other judgment should be passed than that in diseases which need to be treated with anodynes it quiets all suffering without any harm, and relieves all pain, and quenches all fever, and prevents complications in all illnesses."

And Michael Faraday had noted in 1818: "When the vapor of ether is mixed with common air and inhaled, it produces effects very similar to those occasioned by nitrous oxide." But somehow these clues had been missed.

James M. Venable, a young patient of Long's, had two tumors on the back of his neck. Venable, like many others in the village, had inhaled ether for its pleasant effects. In 1842 Long persuaded him to let him remove one of his tumors while he was under ether. When Venable woke up he could not believe that the knife had pierced his flesh until he was shown the excised tumor. He was glad to pay the doctor's fee of two dollars for the operation and ether.

This was the first use of ether in surgery. But no one besides Long, Venable, and several other patients on whom the Georgia doctor used it, knew about it. The small-town doctor, for reasons hard to understand, failed to report the event, while agonizing surgery continued throughout the world.

Yet Long was a man of more than common intelligence. Born in Danielsville, Georgia, in 1815, he was the son of a prosperous plantation owner highly regarded for his business acumen and knowledge of law. When the boy was only five years old he accidentally struck his little sister's hand with an

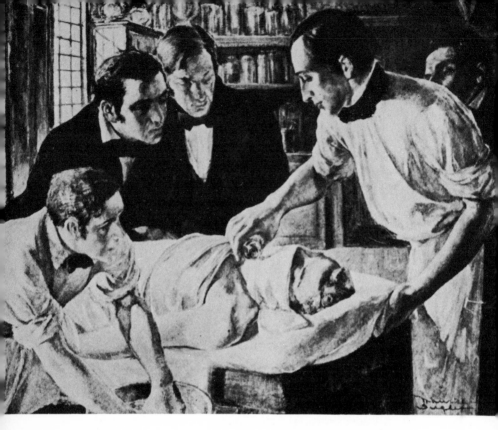

Dr. Long administering ether for the first time

axe, almost chopping off three of her fingers. Showing remarkable resourcefulness for a child, he pushed the fingers
back in place, while the little girl's screams brought their
mother to the scene. She bandaged the fingers in position,
covering the wound with sugar to keep it from being infected.

Crawford attended the school that his father had founded.
When he graduated, at fourteen, he was enrolled in Franklin
College in Athens, later the University of Georgia. He
graduated second in his class and at the age of twenty decided to
study medicine, but his father insisted that he should first
become the principal of the town school for a year.

At the end of the school year Long went on to Lexington (now in Kentucky) to study medicine under distinguished physicians in Transylvania Medical College. In 1837, he enrolled at the University of Pennsylvania, where he received his medical degree after two years. He spent the next eighteen months in New York preparing himself in surgery, at which he exhibited considerable skill.

In 1842, he took over the practice of his first teacher, and married the niece of Governor Swain of North Carolina. He was beginning a comfortable life in a town where the Long family was influential when he performed the operation under ether anesthesia whose importance completely escaped him.

His own explanation, seven years later, for his failure to report his success, was that he wished to satisfy his mind that ether really produced anesthesia, and that it was not just imagination, or a peculiar insensitivity to pain in certain people. He was waiting to see whether some other surgeon had had a similar experience prior to his own. At any rate, by neglecting to tell the world, Long lost the honor of priority of discovery.

In the meantime, in 1844, Horace Wells, a young dentist of Hartford, Connecticut read an advertisement in the *Courant*. One Gardner Quincy Colton (alias for Colt) promised an entertainment with laughing gas that would be "a genteel affair," because only gentlemen would be permitted to inhale the gas. One evening after supper Wells took his wife to the show. A young man under the influence of the gas dashed about the stage, threshing his arms and bumping into furniture until he sank into unconsciousness.

Dentist Wells noticed that the boy had bruised his shins and scraped his knees while going through the strange antics produced by nitrous oxide. The boy later said that he felt no pain from his injuries. The dentist turned to the proprietor of the show with an idea that had just entered his head. "Couldn't this gas be used to deaden the pain in tooth-pulling? I would like to try it."

The next day Colton brought some of the gas to the dentist's office. While Colton administered the gas to Wells, a neighboring dentist pulled out one of his teeth. When he regained consciousness, Wells announced: "It is the greatest discovery ever made! I didn't feel so much as the prick of a pin!"

This seemed to him the perfect pain-killer that should bring him fame and fortune. Without much further testing of his discovery, he took a trip to Boston. First he visited Dr. Morton, his old friend and former partner in dentistry. Morton listened to Wells's enthusiastic report of the pain-killer, but advised caution. He proposed that they seek advice from Dr. Charles T. Jackson, a jack-of-all-trades in science whom Morton had met in the Harvard Medical School. Apparently he had some regard for his friend's opinion. Jackson decided there was no value in nitrous oxide, but Wells was not prepared to abandon his project.

He arranged a demonstration of laughing gas before a group of professors and students at Harvard. A student volunteered for the test, and Wells administered the gas. Somehow the demonstration failed; just as the tooth was yanked out the patient screamed with pain. The surgeon cried, "Humbug." The audience booed loudly, and the dentist fled the hall. Morton, who had assisted Wells, was now convinced that nitrous oxide was ineffective. But Wells

Horace Wells (1815–1848)

went home to Hartford, and successfully used the gas on several patients. Then one patient died. Deeply discouraged, Wells gave up dentistry, trying his hand at other occupations. Everything he tried to do ended in failure. Still trying to capitalize on nitrous oxide, he went to Europe, hoping to obtain a patent for his discovery in France. He finally committed suicide three years after the humiliating demonstration at Harvard.

Nitrous oxide as a pain-killer was temporarily dropped, but in Boston the search for another agent to do what laughing gas had failed to accomplish went on.

William Thomas Green Morton, friend of the tragic Wells, now comes back into our story.

A farmer's son, he was born at Charlton, Massachusetts, August 9, 1819. His early school days were unhappy; he suffered from the harsh discipline and beatings, which it was said affected his health. He left the school and attended two others until, at seventeen, he was finished with formal schooling.

For the next three years he took different jobs, some of them in the publishing business, and joined with partners in business ventures that ended no more happily than his schooling. He then decided to become a dentist. The record is not clear as to where he studied dentistry, possibly in Baltimore, and then as a student under Wells. Between 1842 and 1843 he was Wells's partner in a Boston dental office. There was little money in dentistry, but both Wells and Morton were ambitious. Morton was clever with his hands, and invented a solder for fastening artificial teeth to dental plates. A dental bridge was fine, but seldom fitted comfortably over the roots of decayed teeth. Extraction was painful, and patients preferred to go without plates and hold on to the stumps of their own teeth.

If only they could find a painless way to extract teeth! Then there would be a wonderful market for false teeth set in their fine plates, the two dentists dreamed.

When the Wells-Morton partnership broke up, Wells went to Hartford to practice, and Morton remained in Boston. While maintaining his dental office, Morton took courses in medicine at the Harvard Medical School. It was there that he met Charles Jackson, from whom he learned about ether. The medical students at "ether frolics" derived amusement from the mild intoxication or "ether jag." Jackson had noticed that the inhalation of the vapors made the boys insensible to pain when they fell over the furniture. Jackson had never made use of this knowledge to try ether for relief from pain. But Morton, intent on getting a pain-killer for his dental practice, saw its possibilities.

He began to experiment: First he tried the vapors on insects, worms, frogs, and chickens; then on goldfish and his pet spaniel. The dog sniffed and fell dead asleep. Morton was ready to try it on himself. He seated himself in a chair, holding a watch in one hand. With the other he applied a towel soaked in ether to his nose and mouth. He lost consciousness and, when he came to, seven minutes had clicked away. Surely this was enough time to pull at least one tooth. Like Wells, he had one of his own healthy teeth drawn under ether, and felt no pain.

He was now ready to give ether to a patient. He had the opportunity one night in September, 1846 when a patient rang the bell and walked into his office. His swollen cheek was bound with a kerchief, and he hoped Morton could stop the unbearable pain he had suffered for several days. Could the dentist use this so-called mesmerism on him so that he wouldn't feel the pain of extraction? Morton assured him he had something better — a chemical that would do just that.

The stranger, Eben Frost, agreed to inhale the ether. A minute after he fell asleep the abscessed tooth was out, and the patient had felt nothing. Morton was pleased as Punch, but in his pleasure he didn't forget an important detail. He shrewdly had Frost sign a statement describing what had happened. In part it said: "In an instant I awoke, and saw my tooth lying on the floor. I did not experience the slightest pain whatever. I remained twenty minutes in his office afterward, and felt no unpleasant effects from the operation."

What was more, Morton had his assistant sign another statement saying that he had witnessed the operation, and that Frost had shown no sign of pain during the extraction. The next morning, the daily newspaper reported the story as told to a reporter by the assistant. Doctors shook their heads in disbelief, but Morton's practice picked up. Up to this time, Morton had not revealed what his chemical was.

Morton was obviously a practical man; he realized that he must now convince the profession. Before long he arranged for a public demonstration of ether before the same surgeon, John Collins Warren, who had witnessed Wells's fateful failure with nitrous oxide. Within two weeks after he had extracted Frost's tooth, he received a note from the House Surgeon at the Massachusetts General Hospital. Would Morton administer his "preparation" to a patient who was to be operated on?

Morton was not satisfied with his equipment, and consulted an instrument maker for help. There was no time to be lost, and the instrument maker agreed to get an improved inhaler ready in time for the scheduled operation.

On the morning of October 16, 1846, all but one of the principals were ready in the amphitheatre: Dr. Warren, the senior surgeon, his assistants and strong-armed men who were to hold the patient down, the students, and other spectators were waiting; the patient was brought in, pale with fright. There was no turning back: everything was set for the removal of the tumor on his jaw. Only Morton had not arrived.

Dr. Warren was ready to proceed without him, announcing to the onlookers: "As Dr. Morton has not arrived, I presume he is otherwise engaged." And he was — putting the finishing touches on his inhaler in the instrument maker's shop. Just as the skeptical audience burst into laughter at Dr. Warren's remark, Morton appeared. The operation was held up for a few minutes while Morton prepared a sponge soaked in ether which he placed in the inhaling globe, temporarily corked.

As he came forward to the operating table on which the patient was strapped as always before an operation, Dr.

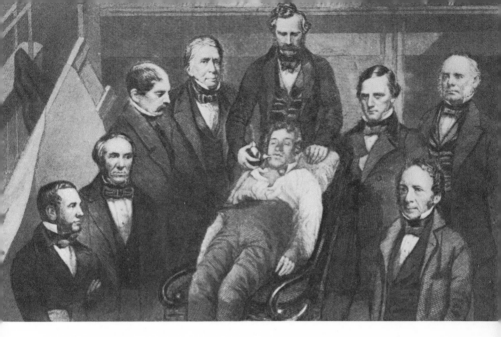

W. T. G. Morton giving ether for the first time at a public demonstration

Warren turned to Morton, saying: "Well sir! Your patient is ready."

But Morton wished to gain the patient's confidence. Pointing to Eben Frost who in gratitude had come along to the hospital, he said to the pale man: "There is a man who has been operated on under this chemical, and can tell you that it worked." Frost gladly complied.

"Are you afraid?" Morton asked the patient.

Whether from courage or confidence, the patient replied, "No, I will do as you tell me."

Morton then put the neck of the flask to the patient's mouth, instructing him to breathe. Slowly the patient went under, his arms and legs jerking in a way probably familiar to frequenters at "ether frolics." As yet no one suspected what the chemical was. After several minutes, the patient was asleep and relaxed. It was now Morton's cue in the drama, as he turned to Dr. Warren.

"Sir, *your* patient is ready."

Warren made the incision. He, like the witnesses, was ready for the bloodcurdling screams so familiar in the operating room. But the patient uttered not a sound.

The operation over, the patient slowly regained consciousness. When questioned by Morton, he readily admitted having felt no pain.

Dr. Warren then broke the silence with the famous words: "Gentlemen, this is no humbug!" And Dr. Henry J. Bigelow: "I have seen something today that will be heard round the world."

The first page of a new chapter in the story of surgery was turned that day.

———

An obscure but ambitious dentist had by this momentous event been thrust into the world limelight. We leave him to pursue his ambition for fame and fortune and return to the British Isles.

In the village of Bathgate, southern Scotland, James Young Simpson was born, seventh son and eighth child of David Simpson the baker, and his wife Mary. It was June 7, 1811. It can only be assumed that there was something very special about little James because despite their poverty and the seven other mouths they had to feed, the Simpsons decided quite early that their youngest would have an education.

And so it was. The "very, very young . . . very poor, and almost friendless" boy found himself, at the age of fourteen, a student at Scotland's famous University of Edinburgh. He had no idea where his studies would lead him, for he enrolled as an art student. Somewhere along the way he entered the medical school, graduating as Doctor of Medicine when he was twenty-one.

James's parents had not skimped and struggled for nothing. Their son had not only become a doctor, but on graduation was awarded an assistantship to James Hamilton, Professor of Midwifery. A century after Willie Smellie and William Hunter had stormed the impregnable fortress held by women, a man still had to fight his way into the field of obstetrics. But Simpson chose to take this hard road. When Professor Hamilton died, the bright and confident young man (now twenty-eight) applied for his chair at the university. A bitter battle was waged by the contestants for the position, their supporters, the professors, and the town council. The professors objected to Simpson for reasons that had nothing to do with his competence. He was young, a poor baker's son, and single.

Simpson could hardly help his youth and the circumstances of his birth, but he managed to confound the rival camp by suddenly announcing his engagement to Jessie Grindlay, a lady from Liverpool. Whether or not this turned the election in his favor is hard to say, but he received seventeen votes to his opponent's sixteen.

After returning from their honeymoon, Professor Simpson and his wife settled in Edinburgh where Dr. Simpson's office was filled with patients. His wife entertained famous visitors from every corner of the earth, whom her husband irresistibly attracted. Dr. Simpson was no ordinary doctor. He was an innovator in his chosen field. He lectured brilliantly and wrote voluminously on many obstetrical subjects. But his part in our story deals with his revolutionary idea that women in labor need not suffer pain. Dr. Simpson not only had to

Sir James Young Simpson

fight the prejudice against men *accoucheurs*, but now stirred up another hornet's nest. For was not woman born to bear anguish in labor? In that very city Agnes Sampson was burned at the stake in 1591 for her heresy in trying to relieve the pain of a lady of high rank in childbirth.

Only three months after the discovery of ether as an anesthetic, Simpson tried it in an obstetric case. But he found that ether irritated the lungs. Convinced, however, that there must be other chemicals that could be substituted for ether, he tried several. He decided on chloroform as the most promising, a chemical that had been prepared in 1830 by Samuel Guthrie, an American surgeon.

One evening Simpson and two of his colleagues decided to put chloroform to the test. The three sat around the table in Simpson's dining room, each supplied with a jarful of the chemical. As they inhaled the vapors they felt exhilarated, and there was an exchange of lively banter. Before long they fell into a deep sleep. When they became conscious they repeated the performance, only this time Simpson's niece decided to join them in the experiment. Just as she was falling asleep, apparently before the others, she repeated several times "I'm an angel. Oh, I'm an angel."

Shortly after this test Simpson gave chloroform to a woman during childbirth. The woman, in a previous difficult birth, had been in labor for three days. This time the baby was born within half an hour after the mother was anesthetized. She was not roused by the baby's first cry. When she awoke she said that she had enjoyed a good sleep. It was no easy thing "to convince the astonished mother that the labor was entirely over and that the child presented to her was really her 'own living baby,' " Dr. Simpson said in his report of the case in 1847.

Immediately he brought down the wrath of the clergy on his head. Simpson and his pain-killer were denounced from the pulpit. Chloroform was an invention of the devil! Simpson handled himself very well in this part of the controversy. His paper, *Answers to the Religious Objection Against the Employment of Anesthetic Agents in Midwifery and Surgery*, ended with an allusion to the first operation described in Genesis. "And the Lord God caused a deep sleep to fall upon Adam, and he slept: and he took one of his ribs, and closed up the flesh instead thereof." With cool logic he brought forth one argument after another for humane surgery.

The objections to anesthesia were not solely on religious grounds. His colleagues raised an even greater storm. Childbirth without pain, they cried, was not "natural" or "physiological." A mother who did not suffer the pangs of labor could not love her child. Simpson fought these objectors with clear reasoning. But the most potent weapon against those who would hold back progress was that more and more

people underwent anesthesia. Within two years after Simpson's paper was published many thousands of people in Edinburgh alone had been given chloroform during childbirth
and surgery.

When in 1853 Queen Victoria took chloroform for the
delivery of her seventh child, Prince Leopold, there was
much medical headshaking about the "awful responsibility"
her attendants had undertaken. But the Queen had been won
over, and four years later she again accepted the anesthetic
during labor. Thus royal approval of the practice finally
silenced the opposition.

———

In the meantime a different kind of battle was going on in
the birthplace of anesthesia, America. Who really discovered
ether?

Lancet, England's venerable medical journal, wrote: "The
discovery of Dr. Morton will undoubtedly be placed among
the blessings of human knowledge and discovery. That its
discoverer should be an American is a high honor to our
transatlantic brethren; . . ."

Even before the famous demonstration at the Massachusetts General Hospital, Jackson had urged Morton to apply
for a patent. The trade name given to ether was Letheon
(for the mythical waters of Lethe that wiped out memory
of pain). Morton did so, agreeing to give Jackson ten per
cent of the profits. But Jackson, not wishing to gamble on a
possible failure of the demonstration, withdrew from the
agreement, gave up all claims to future profits, and settled
for $500 for his advice.

The patent was granted after a few weeks; Morton then
told his secret to Drs. Warren and Bigelow, and the story of

ether anesthesia was reported by the latter in a Boston medical journal. Jackson once again reneged on his agreement, and announced himself as the sole discoverer of anesthesia. Wells, back from Europe, also had pressed his claim in the Hartford *Courant*. The get-rich-quick bug had infected all three. Ironically, none of them was to realize any monetary advantage.

Within the next three years, ether anesthesia, with Morton's inhalator, was used by surgeons, dentists, and hospitals without royalties to the inventor of the inhalator. Even the Army and Navy in the Mexican War failed to pay him. Morton petitioned Congress for an award, with the backing of Senator Stephen Douglas. But Jackson claimed priority and piously asserted that he had given up his share of the patent because he sought no profit from suffering. Wells's widow insisted that the award should go to her. By this time Dr. Long's use of ether in Georgia had also become known, but he was willing to abide by the decision of an investigating medical society.

In all this confusion among the contestants for the honor and money — Europeans also becoming involved in this inglorious controversy — Morton never received a penny. He went to live on a farm, but the whole unsavory wrangle preyed on his mind. Petition and litigation brought him to New York countless times on his way to Washington. On one of these trips he suffered a complete breakdown, and was taken to St. Luke's Hospital, where he died in poverty and despair in 1868, twenty-two years after his dramatic Boston demonstration. A dozen years later Jackson died in an asylum for the deranged.

In the years that followed the unfortunate controversy, the world remembered its benefactors:

The University of Pennsylvania, Long's alma mater, hung a bronze plaque in the medical building which reads: "To Long, First to Use Ether as an Anesthetic in Surgery." Danielsville, his birthplace, and Jefferson, his later home, erected monuments in his honor, and nearly a century after the event for which he is remembered, the United States issued a postage stamp bearing his name.

Horace Wells is commemorated by a memorial in Bush-

Monument to Horace Wells in Paris, France

Ether Monument, Public Garden, Boston, Mass. "Neither shall there be any more pain." — Revelations

nell Park, by a carved pew in Trinity College, Hartford,
Connecticut, and by a statue in Paris.

In England, grateful Queen Victoria knighted Simpson.
Upon his death in 1870 he was buried with honors in Edinburgh, although there was a place for his remains in Westminster Abbey. The shops and banks shut down and throngs
followed the funeral procession in sorrowful homage to a
great battler for anesthesia.

In America, Boston claimed Morton as its hero. Harvard
University awarded him an honorary degree. Massachusetts
General Hospital, which still celebrates October 16th as
"Ether Day," sent him a silver bowl and a cash prize of
$1000. The city erected a beautiful monument in his honor.
The table on which he demonstrated the surgical use of ether
is preserved in the cupola room of the hospital where the
wonderful event took place.

CHAPTER NINE

Clean Wounds

Pain in surgery was forever banished. It was at last pos-
sible for surgeons to perform operations on diseased internal
organs, using delicate procedures that did not depend on
lightning speed. But a deadly hazard still threatened the
surgical patient — wound fever, the enemy that travels on
dirty hands.

Picture a scene in an operating room about the middle
of the nineteenth century. The patient is fully clothed in his
street garments. The surgeon makes his appearance in a
frock coat, high collar, and cravat. In the fashion of the
time, he sports a flowing beard, side whiskers, or at least a
full mustache. The assistant has his coat sleeves rolled up and
perhaps wears an apron; the instruments are scattered on an
uncovered wooden table. Students watching the operation
crowd around the patient for a clear view of the operation.

Where are the spotlessly white amphitheatre, the sterilized
gowns and caps? Where the sterile gloves and the gauze
masks? And what about the endless scrubbing, washing, boiling, sterilizing, and swabbing so familiar today?

The hidden enemy that lurked in every corner of the

operating room a century ago claimed its victims in the form of *septicemia* — infection carried into the wound, and through the blood to every part of the body. This enemy had still to be conquered.

The first man to wage a solo battle against this dread enemy found himself embroiled in a bitter life-long struggle with those who should have been his warmest allies — the surgeons themselves. This unsung hero was a Hungarian doctor, Ignaz Philipp Semmelweis.

He was born in Budapest in 1818, the fourth son in a family of eight children. Ignaz's father was a shopkeeper who gave his children as good an elementary education as Budapest provided in those days. Whatever else he may have learned, schooling certainly left the youth with an aversion to wielding the pen. Semmelweis so hated to write that he lacked a very important weapon later in life when he was not able effectively to spread his views about the combatting of infection in wounds.

It was quite by accident that he turned to medicine. At nineteen he was a law student at the University of Vienna, with little interest in the subject. One day he wandered into the dissection room of the Vienna General Hospital where a professor was developing a new branch of medicine. He was dissecting bodies with diseased organs. Today we call this pathological anatomy, but in those days it was still a novel idea to examine systematically the changes made in the organs by disease, and relate them to the patient's symptoms.

Semmelweis was so much interested in what he saw that day that he dropped his law studies and switched to medicine. He received his medical degree in 1844, and soon afterwards a master's degree in midwifery as well. Then he had his first disappointment. He was offered a post as assistant in Vienna's Obstetric Clinic, but the appointment was suddenly given to another student. There was nothing to do but to wait for another appointment. During the two years he had to wait, he cultivated the friendship of two professors who were developing specialties. Dr. Skoda evolved the method (still in use) of diagnosing chest diseases by tapping on the chest with the end of the finger, and Dr. Hebra did pioneer work in skin diseases. In his later reverses, Skoda and Hebra were two friends on whom Semmelweis could count.

The Obstetric Clinic to which he was finally appointed had two sections. In the section where the medical students were trained for midwifery, one out of every ten mothers died from puerperal fever, and sometimes this toll in childbirth was 30 per cent. In the other section, where the midwives were trained, the deaths were far fewer. Puerperal fever was thought to be an epidemic disease, produced by "miasma" — poisonous matter in the air, or other atmospheric or soil conditions. Some people even believed that it was due to the emotional strain prospective mothers underwent because they were examined by male students. Foreign students were excluded because it was thought they were rougher in their examinations than the Viennese.

The medical students' section had such a bad reputation that patients assigned to it would kneel, wring their hands, and beg that they be sent to the section in charge of the midwives. Semmelweis later described the terror of these mothers, their hearts beating so rapidly that the pulse could not be counted, their tongues dry, and their abdomens swollen. At death's door, they pleaded to be released from the hospital. Several times a day the priest, preceded by a choir-boy tinkling a bell, would come to the hospital to give the last

Ignaz Philipp Semmelweis

sacrament to the dying. "The bell, in fact, became for me an exhortation to search with all my energies in order to elucidate the cause," Semmelweis said.

The young doctor refused to believe that epidemics had anything to do with the difference in the death rate in the two sections of the ward. Once a light-hearted student, he now pored over books and strained to find an explanation for the misery he saw around him. Day after day he and his students went to the dissecting room to study the bodies of the mothers who had died. Always he found the swollen liver, spleen, kidneys, lymph glands, and even the meningeal membranes covering the nervous system, inflamed and pus-ridden. From the dissecting room, he went directly to the ward to examine patients in labor. In his determination to find the cause of death he conducted his examinations too thoroughly. The result was that even more women died.

Semmelweis drove himself night and day. He talked about the problem with his colleagues, and especially with Professor Kolletschka, whom he met at work over a cadaver every morning. Why the difference in the death rate in the two sections? The women came from the same poor sections of the city, the conditions in the hospital were the same (in fact, they were worse in the midwives' section, which was over-crowded), the methods of delivery were alike. Then why more childbed fever in his section? Was it that the midwives were gentler in their handling of the patients? He tried to be gentler in his examinations. Fear of death might be responsible, so he asked the priest to dispense with the bell-ringing. But nothing helped, and the deaths mounted. By 1847, the sensitive young doctor was so overwrought that his superior suggested a change of scene for him.

Semmelweis took a trip to Venice, but a vacation away from the sight of suffering and dying women was no help. He could not run away from the distressing problem that had become a part of his being. Within three weeks he was back in Vienna and at his accustomed place in the dissecting room. The place next to him, ordinarily occupied by Professor Kolletschka, was vacant. The stunned Semmelweis learned that while he was away his colleague had died.

The tragic death of Professor Kolletschka had come sud-denly, after his finger had been nicked with a scalpel by an awkward student during a post-mortem examination. The following night the professor shook with chills and high fever. His death was caused by blood poisoning. When Semmelweis read the autopsy report he was struck with the similarity of his friend's symptoms with those of childbed fever: suppuration, swollen lymph glands, inflamed pleurae and peritoneum. He had reported the identical symptoms in countless women who had died in the Obstetric Clinic.

It suddenly became crystal clear: puerperal fever was the same as wound fever. The knife that pierced the professor's flesh had carried with it poisonous matter from the cadaver. Was Semmelweis himself introducing this poison every day into the bodies of his patients, carried on his fingers from the dissecting room? And weren't his students also carrying infection on their dirty hands to the mothers in labor? The thought was agonizing to the sensitive doctor, yet the facts explained much that had never been clear before.

The much higher death rate in his ward must be due to the fact that the medical students did dissections, while the midwives did not. Women who had easy labor and needed little assistance usually escaped the fever, while women who struggled for several days and received several examinations were much more vulnerable. "It is owing to the doctors that there is so high a mortality in childbed," he stated. Nor did he spare himself: "As a logical outcome of my conviction I have to acknowledge that God only knows how many women I have prematurely brought down into the grave."

His troubled conscience drove him nearly insane, but he immediately went about remedying the murderous procedure in the hospital. He made it a firm rule that all doctors were to wash their hands with chlorine water before entering the maternity ward. Semmelweis knew nothing about germs, because this was thirty years before Louis Pasteur would show the relation of microbes to disease. But he insisted on the hand-scrubbing and washing in the basin of chlorine water that was placed at the door of the ward.

During the next several months the mortality went down to less than a fourth of what it had been before. This should have been reason enough for everyone to continue the simple procedure. But from his supervisor down, there was grumbling about the senseless business of washing. Only Skoda and Hebra saw that Semmelweis had a point. The others fought him. They repeated parrot-like the old ideas of "epidemic," "miasma," and "fear" as the causes of childbed fever. Semmelweis fought back like a maniac. "Murder," he shouted. "The murder must cease," he wrote to a recalcitrant *accoucheur*. His sharp words did not make his idea any more acceptable; they only brought down abuse on his head.

When it became clear to him that infection was spread not only from cadaver to patient, but from patient to patient, he insisted on the washing procedure between each examination. But that only increased the resistance to the efforts of a "fanatic."

His two friends urged Semmelweis to write up his findings and his simple method of saving mothers. But the thought of writing paralyzed him. Hebra wrote up his experiments for him, and the paper was published, but everywhere obstetricians and surgeons were indifferent.

Because of Semmelweis's own efforts, the death rate went down, and for two months there was not a single death from puerperal fever in his section of the ward. Still the petty persecution continued, and Semmelweis, disappointed and bitter, suddenly left Vienna and returned to Budapest. His successor at the Vienna clinic promptly abolished his regulations.

In Budapest he became temporarily resigned to working

as a general practitioner. But then one day in 1851 he visited St. Roch's Hospital, where he saw the usual antiquated practices and the twin evils of dirt and death. He applied for a position as Chief of the Maternity Division, and received an honorary appointment without pay. Once more he threw himself into his crusade with the old fervor. And while his practices brought results, and less than 1 per cent of the patients died from childbed fever, he met with the same stubbornness, scorn, and insult from his colleagues.

But with each unnecessary death Semmelweis made new discoveries. He found that infection could be spread by unclean bed linen. When he happened to see a new patient brought to a bed on which the linens were soiled with the discharges from another who had died with the fever, he stripped off the soiled linen. One day, in a rage, he flung the dirty sheets on the desk of the hospital supervisor. He went on a crusade of cleanliness in the wards. Single-handed he continued the good fight.

In 1855 he was appointed Professor of Obstetrics at Budapest University. In this more important position he felt that he should try to spread his ideas in writing. With the help of an old friend from Vienna he wrote a little booklet outlining the causes and prevention of puerperal fever. It made up in straightforwardness and the recital of a simple truth for its lack of polished style. The booklet received little recognition in his own day, and its author was again disillusioned by the blind ignorance of his profession. His raging outcries against the evil practices of his time only gained him his dismissal for his "lack of moderation."

Things went from bad to worse for the distraught Semmelweis. He became incoherent, went into rages, and finally became uncontrollable in his derangement. His unhappy wife wrote for help to his old Professor Hebra, who had the sad duty of taking him to an insane asylum.

Here he met the same fate as befell his friend Kolletschka. At his last delivery of a sick woman he had accidentally cut his finger. Through the wound the infection spread to the rest of his body. At the age of forty-seven, in 1865, he died from septicemia, the disease he gave his life to conquer.

Without knowledge of Semmelweis's work, his tragic life and death, another pioneer, in England, was now embarking on the same quest for safe surgery.

Joseph Lister, born only nine years after Semmelweis, in 1827, began life with all the advantages the Hungarian doctor had lacked. In his prosperous Quaker home there was an atmosphere of simplicity and devotion to science and learning. Joseph's mother, Isabella Harris, was a school supervisor, and his father, Joseph Jackson Lister, was a successful wine merchant whose real interest was in science.

Studies in mathematics and optics led Mr. Lister to his chief contribution to the scientific world: the improvement of the compound microscope invented by Zacharias Janssen two centuries earlier. The relic made blurred and off-color images, and had never been a useful tool. Now Lister put the lenses together in such a way that a clear image was obtained, making possible the discovery of the cell as a separate living unit. Later it proved invaluable to Pasteur and others in the study of microbes. Lister was honored for this work by being made a Fellow of the Royal Society.

Young Joseph, the fourth child and second son of the family, breathed the atmosphere of science from the first, and even in early childhood he announced that he was going

Joseph Jackson Lister (Joseph Lister's father) from a photograph by Maull and Co., London

Joseph Lister at 13. Silhouette by his father

to be a surgeon. In the Quaker schools where he was an earnest pupil, science was a regular part of the curriculum — unusual in that day, and a boon for Joseph. By the time he was fifteen he was well grounded in mathematics, modern languages, and natural science, and had a fair knowledge of the bones and of anatomy.

His father was pleased with Joseph's interest in natural science, but did not encourage his ambition to become a surgeon. "Let nature do her own work," he would say. But as his son's bent became more obvious, no obstacle was put in his way, and the family accepted his choice of career.

At seventeen Lister was enrolled in the nonsectarian University College of London, one of the few schools that admitted the Friends. In 1847 he was granted the B. A. degree, and immediately went on to study medicine in the same institution.

Lister was lucky in his teachers. There was Robert Liston, who could hold up the femoral vessels and amputate a thigh in twenty-eight seconds. He was also the first British surgeon to perform a major operation under ether. Since this happened at the university hospital during the year when Lister began his medical studies, it is altogether possible that he was a witness on the historic occasion. Wharton Jones, who is known for his investigations of inflammation, and William Sharpey, the first to teach physiology as a separate course, were others of Lister's celebrated teachers.

When Lister was a medical student, conditions in the surgical wards were the same as those that faced Semmelweis in the Obstetrical Clinic in Vienna. Recalling these days at the first Lister Memorial Lecture at the Royal College of Surgeons, years afterwards, Sir Wm. Watson-Cheyne, Lister's one-time student, said: ". . . a surgical ward in a hospital was a place in which most patients were visibly ill, with flushed faces, parched lips, delirium, severe pain, etc., and many of them were evidently on the verge of death; the wards were pervaded with a peculiar mawkish odour which was very trying to newcomers." These patients were suffering with "septic" diseases, surgical gangrene, and septicemia.

Lister's introduction to the horrible aftermath of surgery in those days came when he worked as dresser in the surgical wards of University College Hospital. His first patient had a spreading gangrene, one of the worst kinds of tissue ravishers. This made a deep impression upon Lister. He began to think that nothing was more urgent than discovering the cause of gangrene and finding a way to treat it. As he assisted the surgeons in their attempts to check the creeping decay of healthy flesh around the wounds, he wondered about the vague explanations, hardly more than guesses, given for its cause. If exposure to oxygen was responsible, then why didn't gangrene occur in all wounds?

He scraped some of the grayish material from a wound, and spread it on a slide. Though he could see nothing under the microscope that would give him an answer, Lister was convinced that oxygen was not the cause of wound infection. It was decades before Koch showed how to stain tissues to make microbes visible.

When Lister graduated in 1852, Professor Sharpey, who had traveled to different medical schools, advised him to go to Edinburgh to work for a while under James Syme, the surgeon who had bitterly fought Simpson during the early chloroform days. Lister was warned about the quarrelsome doctor, but either Syme had changed or Lister's mild manner disarmed him, for the two liked each other from the start. He had expected to remain in Edinburgh only a month, but

James Syme, noted surgeon and Lister's father-in-law

when Syme invited him to prolong his stay, Lister agreed. He was to remain there for seven years.

Young and handsome but quiet and dignified, side-whiskered Lister was a frequent visitor at the home of Dr. Syme, where he met his eldest daughter Agnes. Agnes was a serious, highly intelligent young lady. Her attraction was not in her looks, for she was rather plain. She dressed soberly,

and her dark straight hair was parted in the middle and
brushed neatly to frame her face. Her quiet manner and
serious outlook on life must have appealed to the earnest
young man. Agnes, as much as the vacancy at the Edinburgh
Infirmary, must have made him decide to apply for the position of assistant surgeon there. This meant that he would
relinquish his plans for a London practice, and be separated
from his father, who continued to be an inspiration to him.
He wrote home explaining that he wished to work under
Syme, stressing the professional opportunities. If his fondness
for Agnes was another reason, he wasn't yet ready to admit
it. Besides, there was the matter of his Quaker faith. To
marry Agnes, he would have to break with his religion, since
Agnes belonged to the Anglican Church. This was called
"marrying out of the Society," which usually led to
disownment.

Before beginning his new duties, Lister took a trip to
France to familiarize himself with surgical techniques in the
Paris hospitals. When he returned his mind was made up
about Agnes and after a proper interval he asked Agnes's
father for his daughter's hand in marriage. They were married in 1856 in the bride's home. It is said that Dr. John
Brown of Edinburgh, in congratulating the pair at the wedding feast, mentioned an illness that Agnes Syme had suffered
in childhood when she was unconscious for several days.
"Lister is one who, I believe, will go to the very top of his
profession, and as for Agnes, she was once in heaven for three
or four days when she was a very little child, and she has
borne the mark of it ever since."

The young couple took their wedding trip on the Continent, visiting the most important medical centers, hospitals,
and pathology museums. This was the beginning of Agnes's

Left: Joseph Lister, from a daguerreotype, when he was about 28; Right: Agnes Lister, his wife, from a photograph

lifelong devotion to her surgeon husband. She entered whole-heartedly into his work, and acted as his intimate adviser, secretary, and helpmate.

Curiously enough, when the Listers visited Vienna, no one mentioned Semmelweis, who was then working in forgotten isolation in Budapest. Had the two men met, it is probable that the cause of aseptic surgery would have been furthered. But Lister returned to Edinburgh Infirmary without ever having heard of Semmelweis.

On their return to Edinburgh in the fall of 1856 the Listers settled themselves comfortably in a newly furnished home. Dr. Lister's work as assistant surgeon in the Infirmary required his giving a course of lectures. The little time he devoted to actual practice was largely spent in assisting Dr. Syme.

In his early lectures Lister depended on prepared notes, but gradually dispensed with them as his knowledge broadened, and his presentation became richer. At all times his students were in awe of him. As one of them said: "We knew we were in contact with Genius. We felt we were helping in the making of history and that all things were becoming new."

Like John Hunter, Lister was a surgeon-scientist. In fact, his early studies on coagulation began with the observations of Hunter and Hewson.

Developing the techniques of his art was one thing, but to advance the science of surgery meant exploring new fields. While performing operations under Syme and teaching classes, Lister concerned himself with fundamental matters. His special interest was the problem of inflammation — its causes and prevention. This led him to the study of blood coagulation, which had a bearing on normal healing of wounds. His first paper on coagulation of the blood was published in *Philosophical Transactions* in 1858. For this work he was elected a Fellow of the Royal Society in 1860, unusually young to receive that honor.

In 1861 he was appointed Professor of Surgery at the Glasgow Royal Infirmary. Now on his own, he was no longer overshadowed by the great Dr. Syme. As he went to address his first class of nearly two hundred students, instead of the six or seven he had taught at Edinburgh, Agnes was a little nervous. "Oh! I trust he may be blessed, and believe he will be," she wrote to Joseph's mother. Apparently everything went off well, for his father-in-law, congratulating him in a letter wrote: "It being now established that you can please a large class as well as a small one — or I should rather say still better — the game may be considered in your own hands."

In some appropriate place in every lecture, Lister, like his great predecessors, Paré and Hunter, reminded his students of the attributes every doctor should have: a warm loving heart and earnest devotion to truth. These he himself possessed in abundance.

Lister was by this time definitely convinced that sepsis (infection) was closely tied up with putrefaction or poisoning of the blood. How was this putrefying process to be prevented? If indeed the "miasmas" or poisonous gases in the air had something to do with it, the only thing he could do was to keep the wound as clean as possible. But ordinary cleanliness proved to be not enough.

By this time Pasteur had shown the world the role of bacteria in fermentation and putrefaction. Lister became familiar with the Frenchman's work about 1864 when Thomas Anderson, Professor of Chemistry at Glasgow, showed him an article by Pasteur. Lister immediately saw fermentation as the clue to the cause of suppurating wounds. So it was not the gases of the air that the surgeon had to fear, but the minute particles floating in it and settling on the wound. Lister gradually became convinced that if these particles could be kept away from the wound there would be no putrefaction. Boiling killed these living particles, but one couldn't boil the tissues as one could scour instruments and bandages.

Lister's first clear-cut decision was to prevent the entrance of living germs into the wounds by destroying them before they established a footing. If some did get in, it was necessary to inhibit their growth and prevent their spreading. He decided that the best place to test his idea was in compound fractures, those in which the skin was broken along with the bone. By the time such wounds came before the surgeon, they had already been infected during the accident, and so were more likely to become septic. He then looked about for a chemical that would kill germs. He had read a newspaper article that reported the effect of carbolic acid on the sewage in the town of Carlisle. Not only was the foul odor eliminated, but the cattle that fed on the polluted sewage were thereby protected against disease, the article said.

Lister obtained some of this chemical which was sold as German Creosote, and prepared to try it. He had to wait many months for the first compound fracture to come to his attention. In the meantime he repeated some of Pasteur's experiments and devised some of his own.

His plan for preventing sepsis was simple enough. He would apply carbolic acid to the torn tissues and broken bones. Of the eleven cases on which he reported in his first paper, only two developed the hospital gangrene, a smaller number than in untreated wounds. But even these two failures could be explained. In one he had not applied the carbolic acid, in the other sepsis broke out in a small wound that had escaped his attention and had not been treated.

Lister learned a number of other things about normal wound healing. In the wounds that were soaked with carbolic acid, a blood clot formed which did not shrink and disintegrate as such clots had in the past. Instead it formed a firm patch, uniting the sides of the wound. When he examined a bit of this clot under the microscope he saw a tangle of fine connective tissue fibers, and at later stages blood vessels also developed. He noticed that bits of dead tissue were caught up in the tangle of fibers, and after a while these seemed to have dissolved in the clot. This later gave him the idea of using absorbable catgut as ligatures to unite the edges of the wound.

After two or three weeks of healing, the thin layer of clot could be lifted at the edges; below was the beginning of newly grown scar tissue without any signs of infection. This process of healing by blood clot in places where torn tissue could not be brought together was an entirely new discovery.

From then on Lister developed his technique of aseptic surgical dressing. The dresser got on his knees at the side of the bed and squirted carbolic acid from his hand spray. Then Lister himself would lift the first of eight layers of dressing on the wound and pass it to the observers crowding around the patient. Each in turn would smell the bandage to convince himself that there was no putrefaction. Then the layer below was handed around to be examined for the absence of pus. Finally came a protective layer which, when carefully lifted, exposed the delicate but solid and firm clot that was nature's way of healing.

All this while the poor dresser kept pumping the spray, no matter how tired his wrist and arm became.

From the treatment of fractures Lister went on to perform all kinds of operations using antiseptics. Since his main object was to make surgery safe from infection, he was reluctant to write up the actual daring operations in which he employed new techniques. What if someone less careful than he in following the strict antiseptic routine should repeat the operation with dire results? First, he would have to demonstrate to the world that surgical wounds could be kept from becoming infected.

Lister had his reasons for hammering away at the need for antisepsis. The surgical world, especially in England, was divided between the Listerians and non-Listerians. What silly nonsense was this, to douse the patient with carbolic acid, to spray the walls, soak the instruments, and irritate the surgeon's hands with repeated washings in the disinfectant! In this era of wet antiseptic surgery, the air in the operating room was indeed dense with the poisonous carbolic acid mist; the surgeons often wore rubber aprons and boots while operating.

The dyed-in-the-wool conservatives didn't believe that all this foolish chasing of germs prevented suppuration! Among Lister's bitterest enemies was James Simpson, who had apparently forgotten the battles he himself had fought in defense of chloroform. He even accused Lister of appropriating the carbolic acid idea from a French investigator.

While Lister was not the first to use carbolic acid, and never claimed to be, the idea of antisepsis based on Pasteur's researches in bacteriology was brand new. His method of keeping the wound aseptic from the time the skin was broken to the last stage of healing revolutionized surgery. But Lister was not one to engage in debate and controversy. He was a sensitive man, and found strife hateful. He continued his work, improved his methods, trained and inspired his students and everyone else who came with an open mind.

Writing to his father in 1867 about Simpson's accusations he said: "I think I have now said all that I am called upon to say, and if I feel sure of that I shall be willing to let people think and talk as they please, and devote myself with fresh ardour to the work that remains to be done in the way of perfecting the methods of treatment. . . . I quite agree with what thee says about perfect candour in a discussion of this kind. But the truth is I never thought of such a thing as any merit attaching to happening to be the first to *apply* carbolic acid, whether to a sore, a wound, a fracture, or an abscess."

With Agnes taking notes from his dictation, he worked in a laboratory in their home, where he conducted experiments in the evenings. He repeated Pasteur's famous experiment with the gooseneck flasks. This was designed mainly as a dramatic demonstration to accompany his lectures.

He put urine, an excellent breeding medium for bacteria, into four flasks. In three of them he heated the necks until the glass became flexible. Then he drew them out into narrow, tapering tubes which he bent over on themselves. In the fourth flask he cut the neck short without narrowing it. Then he boiled the urine in all four and left them standing. The narrow bent necks excluded dust and microorganisms from the three long-necked ones; the short open neck of the fourth flask permitted their entrance. The urine in the three flasks remained clear and free of microbes for weeks and months, while that in the fourth became clouded with bacteria and molds within a day or two.

Lister experimented with different preparations of carbolic acid. The substance he used at first was impure and did not dissolve easily in water. Undiluted, it was irritating to the tissues. When he obtained a purer specimen, it dissolved readily in water up to one part of the acid in twenty parts of water. He found it was less active dissolved in linseed oil than in a watery solution.

Then there was the problem of satisfactory ligatures. Silk and whipcord commonly in use caused the wound to suppurate. As the ligature rotted away, the blood spurted out from the blood vessel the ligature was supposed to hold together. Frequently the patient died from hemorrhage several days after a successful operation. When he soaked the silk threads in carbolic acid, the acid irritated the wound. He looked about for other materials for ligatures that would not introduce infection into the wound and would remain long enough to permit healing.

He recalled that in the course of natural healing by blood clot, the tissues were able to absorb or to "organize" organic particles. After many experiments he found that catgut, made from sheep's intestine, could be rendered thoroughly sterile with melted wax and its strength increased by aging.

The catgut experiments were carried over into a holiday that he spent with his parents. With the help of his nephew, Rickman Godlee (later his biographer), he chloroformed a calf and sewed up an incision with sterile aged catgut. A month or so later, the calf was killed, and the tissue around the ligature was removed and sent to him in Glasgow to examine. The ligature had not only held the wound together but in time had been absorbed by the tissues.

This led Lister to the further conclusion that after the ligature was tied, the ends should be clipped close to the tie. The reason: the dangling threads became a route for infection to

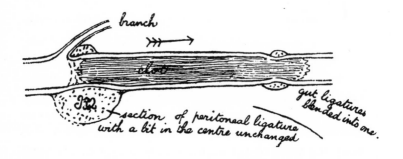

Lister's own drawing showing how the ligatures had been replaced by living tissue of the calf's carotid artery

spread into the wound. It was with great difficulty that he overcame the resistance from surgeons who had been accustomed to pulling out the ligatures after a few days (because they had rotted in the wound). If the wound is kept aseptic, and the ligature cut short, it will eventually be absorbed as healing progresses, Lister repeatedly taught.

In the nine years Lister spent in Glasgow, he established himself as an outstanding surgeon. Knowledge of his works spread as Semmelweis's had failed to do. Glasgow became a mecca for visitors from all parts of Europe and America. Deeply impressed with what they had seen, they returned to their own hospitals and reaped fine results. Lives were saved as the dread septic diseases began to decrease.

By this time his father-in-law, Dr. Syme, had suffered a stroke and was forced into retirement. Lister was the logical man to fill his post at Edinburgh. Sir James Simpson proposed that the chair of surgery be abolished, a strange proposal for the holder of the chair of midwifery. However, the chair was not abolished and Lister did receive the appointment and he and Mrs. Lister packed their belongings and made what turned out to be a happy move. Not trusting the cherished urine bottles to the movers, the Listers carried them with them on the train.

Shortly after their return to Edinburgh, Lister's father died, and soon afterwards Dr. Syme also. Lister felt the loss keenly; both his beloved father and his esteemed father-in-law each in his own way had provided counsel, guidance, and encouragement. During the same year, another important figure died.

With the death of Simpson just prior to Syme, "The two most outstanding personalities . . . had both received unmistakable warnings that their warfare was accomplished. . . .

The removal of these two men, as it were, cleared the atmosphere of the medical world in Edinburgh, and in very different ways affected Lister's position there," wrote Godlee. Each had his supporters, a fact which split the ranks of the profession, and engendered bitter feelings. Now that the principal opponents had gone, the controversy that they had kept alive gradually subsided. According to Godlee "the conflicts of the past were not completely forgotten, but a calmer and more charitable spirit was descending upon Edinburgh, as well as upon the rest of the scientific world." The idea of antisepsis and Lister's fame spread among the younger surgeons.

Lister now settled down to a comfortable position in the university. The number of his pupils swelled with the influx of foreign students. He had an important say in the policies of both the university and the infirmary. His private practice grew, as was to be expected.

In the spring of 1877 Lister received an invitation to go to London as Professor of Clinical Surgery at King's College, the school where he had received his medical education. Had Lister thought only of his personal interest he probably would have declined the appointment, which meant smaller classes, fewer hospital beds, and less opportunity for influencing the policy of the institution. Possibly because London was the stronghold of the older generation of surgeons schooled in the old practices, much of the resistance to his methods emanated from there. But Lister saw this as an opportunity to advance antiseptic surgery in England. While it was a great wrench for him and Mrs. Lister to leave the congenial atmosphere of Edinburgh, he decided to let his enthusiastic students carry on the cause there, and accepted the London appointment.

Once more the Listers, carrying the four urine flasks with them, were on the move. They arrived in London in time for the opening of the winter session in 1877. By this time Lister had become involved in the study of different species of bacteria, and was doing experiments with *Bacillus lactis,* the organism that ferments milk. It seemed to him that the demonstration of a specific organism would be of the highest interest to his audience.

A large group of distinguished surgeons had gathered to hear what Lister had to tell them about the revolution in surgery. But they had to sit through an hour's talk about experiments proving that a particular minute speck of life fermented milk! What did milk have to do with surgery! This was the beginning of Lister's disappointment in London. Of course, his friends had warned him of a cool reception.

He met with the same lack of enthusiasm among his students. No one ran to get a good seat for his lectures as in Edinburgh. A few strolled in leisurely, taking little interest and not bothering to take notes. In the hospital he had to put up with the nurses' old habits and attitudes. The nursing was done by a sisterhood who regarded the wards as their private domain. They resented the intrusion by men in the routine management of the sick rooms. Whoever heard of the doctor dressing wounds? Lister naturally meant to change all that. Nurses were not to meddle with dressings. But it took several years to change the old habits.

One of the assistants Lister brought with him told how they gradually overcame resistance to the new ways. "Not long after we arrived one of the surgeons was going to amputate a limb, and he asked me to come and look after the antiseptic arrangements. His technique was pretty defective, and he did not seem able to visualize the germs which were ready to seize every opportunity of getting into the wound, so I accidentally from time to time squeezed a quantity of carbolic lotion over his hand, for which I was, of course, very apologetic. He did everything that I suggested till it came to tying the vessels, for which he used silk and left the ends long. I begged him repeatedly to cut them short and told him that they would never separate if the wound remained aseptic, but he was adamant: he had never seen a case where the ligature could not be pulled out after a few days, and he was not going to carry out such stupid advice as to cut them short. The wound healed by first intention, except where the bunch of ligatures was, and no suppuration occurred. Day after day I dressed the case for him, and he pulled the threads without success. Gradually he began to think that I had told him the truth, and ultimately I got him to pull the threads as far down as he could and cut them off as high as possible." Fortunately he followed Dr. William Cheyne's instructions to keep aseptic, and "the wound was healed in a few days and no further trouble resulted."

Gradually Lister won over the surgeons.

He continued to experiment with other antiseptics. After Robert Koch, the German bacteriologist, published his work on antiseptic chemicals, Lister began to use mercurial preparations. Finding these irritating to the skin, he impregnated the gauze with a combination of mercury cyanide and zinc, and later this was replaced by bichloride of mercury and iodide of mercury.

Gradually carbolic acid was replaced by other antiseptics, and the carbolic acid spray itself was given up when this was shown to be unnecessary. The organisms in the air were largely harmless and were too few to infect the wound. "Forthwith, the carbolic spray went to the trash heap, grudgingly discarded sea sponges were replaced by those of gauze, blood-stiffened frock coats were relegated to the fire — a veritable surgical housecleaning," is the way a modern surgeon described the passing of the wet antiseptic era with its irritating dousing of patient, surgeon, and operating room.

If the instruments were boiled, and the gauze autoclaved (sterilized by steam under pressure) and applied to clean wounds, infection was not likely. Thorough scrubbing of hands, sterile dressings, and instruments did away with the carbolic acid spray. Other refinements to keep the operating field sterile were gradually introduced. Sterile white gowns, caps, masks, and gloves gradually made their appearance. The new era of aseptic surgery was ushered in.

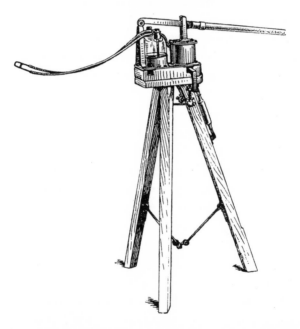

Carbolic acid spray worked by a long handle. It was called the "donkey engine" because it could not be concealed from view when carried in the brougham from house to house

Honors for Lister poured in from all over the world. At a meeting in Philadelphia, the red carpet was rolled out for him. He and Agnes traveled, he lecturing and writing and she acting always as his devoted helpmate. He joined the fighters of anti-vivisection, and helped to pass a bill to permit the use of animals for experimentation. In 1883 he was knighted, despite Queen Victoria's earlier opposition to his vivisection activities.

In 1892, having reached the age of 65, Lister retired from his teaching post and the next year from active surgery at King's Hospital. While they were on vacation in Italy Agnes died, and Lister's buoyant spirit flagged.

But the saddened surgeon did continue with his work in professional organizations. In 1895 he was elected president of the Royal Society. Two years later the Queen bestowed on him the higher title of peer, and in 1902 he received the coveted Copley Medal of the Royal Society. Thus he enjoyed the satisfaction rarely accorded to great men in their lifetime; his work had been accepted and its fruits were everywhere evident.

In the last few years of his life, Lister's health and memory began to fail and he died in 1912, at the age of eighty-five. A public funeral was held in Westminster Abbey, but by his own request he was buried in Hampstead Cemetery beside his beloved Agnes.

CHAPTER TEN

Frontier Surgery

William Worall Mayo, the son of a joiner, or fine carpenter,
was born in the village of Salford, near Manchester, England,
in 1819. His mother was widowed when William was seven,
and though not well off, she managed to give him a good
education. The boy was tutored in French, Latin, and Greek,
and attended a college in Manchester where he studied under
John Dalton, author of the atomic theory. It was Dalton who
stimulated Will's early interest in chemistry.

There had been scientists in the Mayo family as far back
as the seventeenth century, when an ancestor-chemist, John
Mayow, came close to the modern understanding of oxidation,
by attributing the weight gain of a burning substance to its
taking up of "nitro-aerial" particles from the air. Two other
Mayos were well-known physicians in London, so it was not
strange that William favored medicine as a profession. He did
get some experience in Manchester, London, and Glasgow
hospitals, but he was not at it long enough to get a license to
practice.

At the age of twenty-six, Mayo joined the stream of im-
migrants seeking their fortunes in America. He obtained a

position in Bellevue Hospital, in New York, working in the pharmacy and helping out in the wards. After less than two years, he had seen so much misery among the sick poor that he felt the need for a change, and left the hospital.

Like so many other ambitious young men in the forties, William Mayo took to the road, moving west in search of greener fields. His first stopping-off place was Lafayette, Indiana, where in 1848 he and an acquaintance formed a partnership as tailors. The business prospered until one day Mayo met Dr. Elizur Deming, probably as a customer. A cholera epidemic had just broken out, and everyone with any doctoring experience was called upon to help. So less than a year after he had started tailoring, Mayo apprenticed himself to Dr. Deming.

The doctor owned a small medical college in La Porte, about fifty miles north of Lafayette. Typical of the many rural proprietary (privately owned) colleges springing up in the Middle West at that time, it provided medical instruction between the fall harvest and planting time in the spring. Two sessions at one of these schools and three years working with a doctor were the usual requirements for a degree. Mayo qualified for his under Dr. Deming after only one session and a fee of one hundred dollars.

Mayo was in La Porte when he met Louise Abigail Wright, a young woman whose pioneering family had come west in a covered wagon from upper New York State. She was serious-minded, intelligent, and at least the doctor's equal in energy and enterprise. By the time they were married in the winter of 1851, Dr. W. W. Mayo, "Physician and Surgeon," was back in Lafayette, working in the town's drugstore where, for seventy-five dollars a month, he gave medical advice to all customers who asked for it.

The association with Mr. Hart's drugstore lasted only one year after his marriage, when Mayo accepted Dr. Deming's invitation to become his partner. The doctoring business was far from remunerative. Illness — acute, chronic, and epidemic — was rife, but people treated most of their ailments with home remedies and quack preparations. They called on the doctor only as a last resort, and all too often what he had to offer did not inspire enough confidence in the patient for him to be called a second time, if indeed the patient lived long enough for the doctor to make a second visit.

To make up for her husband's uncertain income, Mrs. Mayo rented a store in downtown Lafayette, ordered buckram frames, braids, ribbons, and feathers from New York, and very soon had a flourishing millinery shop. In 1853, when their daughter Gertrude was born, the resourceful woman took on a partner, so that she could fulfill the duties of motherhood as well as those of the "New York Millinery."

The same year, Dr. Mayo was considering taking over the Indiana Medical College in La Porte when Dr. Deming was called to the faculty of the University of Missouri. Mayo immediately changed his plans and went to St. Louis with Dr. Deming. After one winter session as unofficial assistant to the Professor of Anatomy, he applied for and was awarded another M. D. degree.

In the spring of 1854 he returned to his family, intending to start a practice of his own. But again his plans went awry. Lafayette was in a low-lying valley that was flooded every spring, and every summer brought malaria. Dr. Mayo was one of those who annually suffered from malarial chills and fevers. Driven to desperation by one of these weakening attacks, he kissed his wife and baby goodbye, climbed into his buggy and headed his horse west, announcing to the bewildered Louise: "I'm going to keep on driving until I get well or die."

He pushed on to Chicago, and beyond Chicago to the western part of Illinois and the Mississippi. At the great river he met and talked with the frontiersmen and settlers who were on their way north to the Lake Superior region where, they assured him, were untold, unexplored riches, and besides, a healthy climate. Dr. Mayo made up his mind: he too would seek his fortune in the Northwest.

Full of enthusiasm, he went back to Indiana, and persuaded Louise to move to the promised land. In the spring of 1855, carrying in their buggy a fresh stock of millinery supplies and the doctor's few precious instruments and books, the Mayo family set out on the long trek to the Mississippi, where they boarded a steamer heading north to St. Paul.

They found St. Paul a thriving river town and trading center — with more doctors than it could support. Dr. Mayo's chances of establishing a lucrative practice were slim but not disappointing to him, for he had caught the prospecting fever that was driving so many frontiersmen farther north.

Shortly after their arrival a notice in the St. Paul *Daily Minnesotan* announced the opening of Mrs. W. W. Mayo's "Fashionable Millinery." It was now up to her to make a living for the family by fitting hats for the speculators' wives. The doctor was going to prospect for copper.

With a pack on his back, he trudged miles through the forest, eventually staking out a claim on a promising copper deposit. But when his claim was jumped he gave up on copper and started for home. He nearly lost his life when his camping equipment caught fire but, starving and exhausted, he finally made it to St. Paul, partly by canoe on the St. Croix River, the rest of the way on foot.

There followed a new series of ventures: farming, veterinary practice, running a ferry boat, acting as Justice of the Peace — none more successful than prospecting. Such doctoring as he did was paid for in kind: wood, potatoes, perhaps a hen. Then in 1859 Dr. Mayo decided that come what may he would make a go of the calling for which he was trained. He bought a lot in the town of Le Sueur, a couple of miles from where he had farmed, and with his own hands built a house and barn.

Upstairs under the gables of the small, two-storied cottage, he set up his office, furnishing it with a roll-top desk, books, and equipment for mixing medicines. He could count on the few patients he had treated while on the farm, and there was the opportunity of getting new ones among the townspeople in Le Sueur.

The family had now become enlarged by the birth of Phoebe in 1856. A third girl was born in 1859, but she lived only a year. When in 1861 their son William James came, his future as a "great doctor" was taken for granted.

Dr. Mayo's first patient in his new practice was a sick horse. "Why not? I'll see a horse or any other damn thing you've got," he told the farmer. Fortunately the horse recovered, and Dr. Mayo had a good start with the neighbors. But money was still scarce, and for a while he supplemented his earnings by captaining a riverboat carrying crops and timber downstream to St. Paul, and bringing back supplies to the northern settlers. There was also a short-lived career as publisher of the *Le Sueur Courier,* which folded after three months. With the outbreak of the Civil War, Dr. Mayo was appointed examining doctor charged with looking over the Army recruits in Le Sueur County.

When, for the first time, things were beginning to look up

Dr. William Worall Mayo

for the Mayo family, new trouble struck. The uprising of the
Sioux Indians in 1862 threw Dr. Mayo and his townsmen into a
bloody period of massacres and retaliatory hangings. The doctor was awakened in the early hours one morning after delivering a neighbor's baby, and was summoned to the defense

of a nearby village under attack by the Indians. With the rest, he picked up a musket and rode out on his pony. He had fired only a few shots when he realized that his greater duty was with the wounded, who were falling all around him. He ran from one moaning villager to another, bandaging, dressing, patching, and comforting, and when it seemed safe for the outnumbered defenders to evacuate the town, Dr. Mayo arranged for the removal of the injured.

With all the able-bodied men gone, their families seemed to face certain death if attacked. Indeed, the Indians were already gathering on the hill above the town. But according to legend Louise Mayo's resourcefulness and ingenuity saved the day. She sent her two little girls to call the panicky women together and then presented her plan. Following her example, they donned their menfolk's clothes — overalls, trousers, and farm hats — and carrying pitchforks, hoes, rakes, and broomsticks, they marched in formation from the Mayo yard to the village square. There they engaged in improvised maneuvers that from a distance looked like military drill. Her scheme worked: the Indians thought that reinforcements had come, and retreated. The town was saved, with Louise Mayo the heroine of the hour.

On the dark day of reckoning that saw the hanging of thirty-eight Sioux who had led the uprising for food and cash due them from the traders, Dr. Mayo took a "trophy" that later played a part in the advancement of knowledge. When everyone had left the place of execution, he rode out to where the corpses were piled up for mass burial and uncovered the body of the Sioux, Cut Nose. Several months earlier Cut Nose had stolen his pony, but the wiry little doctor had recovered it after a hand-to-hand battle.

He lifted the cadaver into his wagon, brought it home,

Louise Mayo

dissected away the flesh, and preserved the skeleton. This skeleton in the Mayo closet was used years later by the father to teach his two sons (Charles Horace was born in 1865) anatomy of the bones.

A year after the battle with the Sioux, Dr. Mayo was transferred to Rochester, also in Minnesota, as surgeon for its new recruiting station. He welcomed the change because Rochester was a booming town, the end of the road for many weary travelers from the East. The growing population was a great attraction for quack doctors and pill peddlers, but there were also enough patients so that a good doctor could hold his own.

Dr. Mayo's practice, at first cushioned by his small income from the Army, grew substantially during the war years, and when peace came he was well established as the "old doctor" — competent, respected, and devoted to his patients.

No hour was too late and no road too rugged for him to

make his calls, on horseback, by buggy, and on foot, in the blazing heat of summer and in the blizzards and ice-storms of winter. His reputation spread for miles around, and he was regularly called to see patients other doctors had failed to help. Often these cases involved surgery from which others had flinched. He always carried his little bag of instruments, and with the help of a member of the family performed operations on the kitchen table or on a door taken off its hinges and laid across sawhorses. Sometimes, when the patient lived alone, he would stay on to nurse him, split logs to keep the fire going, and prepare a nourishing gruel, or other food. Not before the patient was secure until his next visit would he leave for home or to answer another call.

He was as conscientious, thorough, and advanced as training and the development of medicine in his day would permit. With the clinical thermometer and the wooden stethoscope the only available examining instruments, he depended mainly on his keen observation of the skin, tongue, and eyes, and careful taking of the patient's history, in making a diagnosis. He made urine testing a routine part of his examination, boiling a spoonful over a lamp or candle to test for albumen and sugar with reagents he carried with him. An especially puzzling case would be written up from the day-by-day entries in his book.

In his spare moments he read all of the scant medical news that reached his western outpost of civilization. In 1866, the *Rochester Post* reported at length on "An Important Surgical Operation" performed by Dr. Mayo: Mrs. Titus suffered with an abdominal tumor that endangered her life. She measured 54 inches over the tumor. Dr. Mayo made an opening of about an inch long, and drew from the sack of the tumor "nearly five gallons of a thick, gluey substance." The patient recovered from the operation, which Dr. Mayo ventured to perform after he had read a report of similar operations by Dr. James Sims of Alabama.

————

One night, Dr. Mayo sat down to his evening meal long after the children had gone to bed. He had come home late and Mrs. Mayo had noticed that he stamped the dust off his boots with less than his usual vigor. Now he was lost in thought as he picked at his food.

"Did anything go wrong today?" she asked from across the kitchen table.

Getting no answer, she tried again.

"How did you find Mr. Johnson?"

"What? Oh, that was a strange thing — thought the catheter was clogged . . . " and again silence.

"How did you get along in Norwegian?"

"A neighbor who knew a little English helped out. Couldn't get much of a history. Seems to have been sick about eight weeks."

"Will he get well now?"

"How can I tell? If I could get at the abscess, find out what caused it, but then . . . " the doctor broke off. Plainly puzzled, he was thinking aloud: " . . . had to siphon the flow of pus by suction . . . the thick pus must have been obstructing the bladder ring . . . then a whole quart of bloody urine . . . where can the abscess be . . . will have to put more time in on that case . . . "

Louise recognized the frustration every difficult case brought. She remembered when the farm boy had died after losing his leg. It had been crushed by a falling tree and her husband had amputated. The operation was successful, but the most diligent care by the doctor had not saved him.

"If only we knew how to prevent the spreading gangrene," he had said, over and over again, at that time.

Perhaps the same thought was running through Will's mind now as he went on, "Wonder what those European surgeons would do?"

Louise thought she could follow his train of thought. She frequently read stray medical journals the doctor picked up when he visited St. Paul to attend meetings of the State Medical Society. From these she knew that it was almost five years after Lister's successes with his antiseptic treatment of complicated fractures, before the first vague reports of his carbolic acid spray trickled through to this side of the Atlantic.

"Do you think Lister's method could have saved that boy's leg?" she asked.

As if he had not heard her, Will announced with his customary finality:

"Louise, I must go to Boston or New York — see what the men in the big centers are doing in surgery."

Encouraged by her attention, he continued, "There must be ways to treat the female complaints half the women in Rochester suffer from. Tapping abdominal tumors doesn't cure; they only come back. And then there are . . . "

But realizing that he didn't have to convince her of the gaps in his knowledge, he turned to the practical matters of a trip East. With his family responsibilities, it was a serious proposition, a daring plan; some would have said it was reckless. He had passed his fifty-first birthday and their four children were still young. Despite all their hard work, he and Louise really did not have enough put away to enable him to leave his practice in order to study.

"How much will you need to get by?" he asked.

Louise had somehow managed to look after herself and the children when on other occasions he had acted on impulse with the hope of improving himself and making things easier for the family.

"With what the patients owe you now, we should have enough to see us through," she pointed out.

The doctor's carelessness about his collections had long been a bone of contention, for with him the patients always came first and his account book last. But Louise sensed that this was no time to pursue that subject, and added, only half seriously, "I can always pick up the millinery business again."

"Well, if you really think I ought to go . . . " He left the sentence hanging, and Louise had neither the heart nor the desire to disappoint him.

"It's the only thing to do, Will. Learn what you can of newer ideas about surgery in New York. It will help Willie and Charlie too."

And so in 1870 Dr. Mayo made one of his quick decisions: to suspend his country practice in Rochester, Minnesota, to go to Bellevue Hospital and see with his own eyes what the New York surgeons were doing.

The months he spent in the East were an invigorating professional experience for the Minnesota doctor, giving him the confidence to do surgery more freely. Back home most doctors were general practitioners and shied away from the knife. So many patients were lost that surgery was not highly regarded in the backwoods community around Rochester; many folks would rather die than submit to an operation. But even before his trip, Dr. Mayo had a greater sense of accomplishment from a successful operation than from other forms of treatment that were likely to be only palliative.

On his way home he stopped off at Philadelphia and Lancaster in Pennsylvania to visit the Atlee brothers, who had performed several hundred operations on ovarian tumors. Despite their many successes with this life-saving procedure, it was still generally regarded as foolhardy if not criminal. Ovariotomists were referred to as "belly slitters" along with all others who dared to open up the abdomen. But Dr. Mayo returned to Rochester with increased courage and gradually undertook more and more surgery.

In 1871 Dr. Mayo had a patient with a hernia of the rectum, from which she had suffered for fourteen years. Consultation with a leading Chicago surgeon resulted in the advice that Mayo's proposed operation would only lead to fatal hemorrhage. Having several times tried the more conservative methods of treatment on this patient without success, Dr. Mayo decided to go ahead with his own plan of operation. He succeeded in tying off the circulation so that there was only slight bleeding; then he removed the hernia. The woman quickly recovered, was completely cured, and Dr. Mayo gained additional confidence in his own judgment.

In the Minnesota farming communities, hands, fingers, and legs were frequently caught in reapers, threshers, and other machinery. The only remedy for these injuries was amputation, and in those days people with missing limbs were a common sight. Dr. Mayo had read that James Syme in England advocated repair instead of amputation in such cases: better for a man to have a stiff leg than none at all, he taught. Mending takes longer, but removal of only the diseased part allows the patient at least partial use of the limb. Dr. Mayo took this conservative view to heart, as was indicated by many reports in the local papers.

There was the case of Ole Syvertson from Grand Meadow,

whose arm was broken by the tumbling rod of a threshing machine. "The arm had been set, but the bone did not grow together, and portions of it rotted and crumbled. Dr. Mayo did a bold operation. About four inches of bone were taken out, the ends brought together and a union will take place," the newspaper article read. "The operation was very successful."

Within a few years after his return from New York, Dr. Mayo had acquired prominence as one of only five or six Minnesota gynecologists, doctors of "female diseases." In 1874 he was made chairman of the state society's committee on gynecology. But he had not yet dared to undertake an ovariotomy. When a patient's life was threatened by an ovarian tumor, one of the Atlees was called, because no one in Minnesota considered himself competent to perform the operation.

Then came the case of Mrs. Jacob Waggoner, a woman who lived right across the alley from Dr. Mayo. He had been treating the swelling in her side in the customary way, tapping the growth, and draining off the fluid, but it always filled up again. An infection developed, and the tumor grew to such a size that it interfered with her breathing.

One day Mr. Waggoner, a blacksmith, came for the doctor.

"The missus is in misery again. Will you stop by to see her?" he asked anxiously.

Dr. Mayo found the woman weak, thin, and unable to eat. He took the husband into the kitchen and told him: "Jake, there is nothing to do but cut for it."

"You mean cut her open? But that's dangerous!"

"No more so than doing nothing. She can't live this way."

"Will the operation save her?"

"I can't know for sure, but it's the only thing left. I've

never done it before, but I'm willing to try. Go talk it over with your wife, and let me know."

Because her pain had become unbearable, Mrs. Waggoner chose to take the chance. First Dr. Mayo needed special instruments unavailable locally. He told Mr. Waggoner how to make them, and the blacksmith forged some clamps fitted with hooks made from the teeth of an old mowing machine.

The next day the doctor lined up his operating team: a doctor from the Rochester State Hospital for the Insane, to give the anesthetic; Dr. David Berkman, a veterinarian who had married Gertrude Mayo; and Mrs. Mayo, who often helped him with operations. Willie and Charlie also went along, but had to watch from the doorway.

Dr. Mayo made the incision, inserted a tube into the tumor, and drained the fluid into a tub. Then he placed the clamps, previously heated in a little charcoal furnace, under the tumor, and removed it piece by piece until he had cut out all of the twenty-pound mass. So far so good, but there was still the abscess, and this broke, pouring its contents into the cavity. Dr. Mayo soaked up all he could with sponges and stitched up the incision, leaving a drainage tube.

Eagerly the townspeople read the progress reports on Mrs. Waggoner, who was "doing well." She finally recovered. The editor no doubt voiced the sentiments of the entire state, when he wrote: "We are personally glad . . . for it is not much to the credit of a state like Minnesota to have to send all patients who require difficult and dangerous surgical operations to Chicago for treatment. The citizens of Rochester must feel equally glad with us that there is one amongst us (Dr. Mayo) who has the nerve and courage to undertake to relieve suffering humanity from this dangerous disease."

Fifteen years after Lister had introduced antiseptic sur-

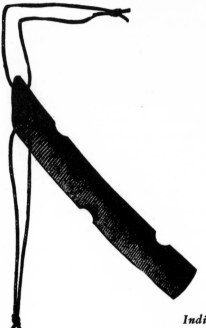

India rubber drainage tube
for treatment of abscesses

gery, "kitchen surgery" was still the rule in the United States. Even in New York, Dr. Mayo had little opportunity to become familiar with Listerism, for it had not been introduced in Bellevue Hospital and infection was taking a horrible toll in the surgical wards.

Surgeons still operated in their street clothes, protecting them with aprons stiff with the blood of previous operations. They sharpened their scalpels on the soles of their boots, carried strings of sutures in their pockets, and needles in the lapels of their coats. They washed their hands *after* rather than *before* they operated.

In the patients' homes, Dr. Mayo could maintain little more than ordinary cleanliness for himself and his instruments, although he fully appreciated the risk of infection. But he had gone far enough in his knowledge to note with pride that a wound healed "almost entirely by primary intention." And his operative skill, gentle handling of the patient, sound judgment, and willingness to try untrodden paths brought him successes despite the many technical deficiencies.

Mrs. Waggoner's operation was but the first of many that made the pioneering Dr. Mayo the leading ovariotomist in his state. Other doctors referred their surgical cases to him and called him into consultation on baffling medical problems. His practice mushroomed and, unable to handle it by himself, he enlisted the help of medical students apprenticed to him.

Busy as he was with his day-to-day practice, the energetic Dr. Mayo was prominent in many professional and public affairs. He organized and was active in the State Medical Society, sparked the effort to establish a city library, worked as a member of the school board for the building of a new school, and arranged for annual public lectures by the abolitionists Wendell Phillips and Horace Greeley. He joined the farmers in their battle to prevent the railroads from continually raising their freight rates, and against the "wheat ring" whose monopoly of grain elevators and warehouses gave it a stranglehold on the small wheat growers.

His sons said of him that he could not bear to stay out of politics: at different times he was alderman, mayor, and state senator. He made some enemies and many friends in his agitation for improvement of the city's water supply, for the building of a city park, a system of sewers, a gas works, and an electric light plant, and in his opposition to the monopoly practices of the railroads and elevator companies.

The people of Rochester selected May 31, 1881, his sixty-second birthday, to express public appreciation of their Dr. Mayo. Presenting him with a five-volume deluxe edition of the *Natural History of the Birds of the United States*, the representative of the donors said in part:

"By night as well as by day, through darkness and storms, you have visited the poor and destitute sick, from whom you never expected to receive any pecuniary remuneration, as freely and as promptly as you have visited those who were able to pay for your services."

This warm tribute came at the peak but not at the end of Dr. Mayo's career. As his sons grew up, became doctors, and joined him in partnership, the "old doctor" led the way in developing frontier surgery into a brilliant period of modern surgery.

CHAPTER ELEVEN

Minnesota's Surgical Twins

"We were reared in medicine as a farmer boy is reared in farming," Dr. Will Mayo often said.

The boys remembered one morning in the seventies when their father, just back from another New York trip, was distributing presents. "And this is the present I would like for myself," he announced, showing them a booklet that pictured the latest model microscope. At a time when many a proprietary medical school made one 'scope do for a hundred students, Dr. Mayo wanted one of his own! Other doctors would have looked upon it as one of those new-fangled toys: "Of what use is it to cure a fever, a drawing abscess, or a bad stomachache?"

Could they afford such a luxury? Louise knew that she would have to postpone buying something she needed for the children or the house, but his heart was set on it. After all, the boys were growing up and could be initiated into its wonders, and in the meantime it would help the doctor in his practice. So she gave in and the luxury became an investment — a six-hundred-dollar investment. To pay for it the doctor secured

Will Mayo and his pony   *Charlie Mayo as a boy*

a mortgage on their house which it is said was not paid off for
ten years.

Willie was twelve and Charlie eight, but not too young to
start learning how to use the instrument. Their father would
set up a specimen he had removed during an operation, focus
the lens and adjust the high power screw, lifting the younger
boy up so that he could peer through the eyepiece. It wasn't
long before they could handle the microscope by themselves,
even fixing, cutting, and mounting the specimens.

Like most Rochester youngsters, Willie and Charlie attended the town's public school, where they did not especially
distinguish themselves, and after school they enjoyed the same
things other boys did. Willie was inseparable from Tony, an
Indian pony — his father's birthday gift when he was eight.
Tony responded to no one but his master and whenever he

could, Willie proudly rode his spirited pet through the streets of Rochester.

While Willie liked the out-of-doors and rough physical activity, the short, stocky Charlie was a tinkerer who liked to make and mend things. Among his youthful achievements was the construction of a telescope, mounted on a tripod on the roof of the house. Under their mother's guidance the boys were introduced into the adventures of star-gazing.

There was plenty of fun for the Mayo children but never any loafing. As soon as they were old enough to do any work, they had to help out around the house or in their father's office. And there was never any question in the Mayo household that the boys would grow up to be doctors.

They loved games, pets, circuses, and boyhood hobbies, but the most memorable part of their childhood was riding with their father on his visits to patients, one or both nearly always sitting alongside him in the buggy. When still very young they learned to hitch up the horses, and would water them while Dr. Mayo was inside a farmhouse tending the sick: it saved him time, he said. After a while they accompanied him to the sickroom and even gave a helping hand with bandaging, putting on a plaster cast, or just holding the lamp while their father was operating.

It was not long before they knew what to ask in taking a history, what to look for in examining the patient, and which remedies to prescribe once the diagnosis was made. If nothing else, these visits must have spared the boys the squeamishness and downright terror that nearly every medical student faces at his first sight of an operation or contact with a cadaver. They came by these experiences naturally, growing up in a home where medicine was part of the family life.

Will was fond of telling the story of the farm boy who

came to deliver eggs and vegetables. As he brought the basket into the kitchen, Dr. Mayo noticed a boil on the boy's neck. Before the unsuspecting young man knew what was happening, the doctor, knife in hand, had lanced the boil. Then the doctor called to his son: "Will, come dress Bill's neck."

Other boys may have played checkers or chess with their father of an evening, but not the Mayo brothers. Out would come the skeleton from the iron kettle for a review of the names of the bones, a lesson in how they were attached to each other, or what their positions were during various types of motion.

A very special event to which the boys always looked forward was an autopsy. As it happened, Dr. Mayo was the town coroner, and this of course gave him an unusual opportunity to perform post-mortem examinations. Willie and Charlie, when not in school, would keep him company, perching on boxes or chairs to see what was going on. What better lesson in human anatomy than to watch the doctor search out this or that organ in the corpse, explaining what he was doing during the examination? And usually he would carry home some interesting bits of tissue to examine under his microscope.

Not all of these visits were routine affairs. There was the time when Will, still in his early teens, accompanied his father to an autopsy late one stormy night. The patient, a caretaker in an abandoned hotel, had lived and died alone. As the doctor and his son entered, the door creaked on its rusty hinges, and the windows rattled as a gust of wind blew through the open door. The doctor lit the kerosene lamp on the table next to the iron cot where the body lay, and went to work. Will looked on, occasionally handing his father the instrument he knew he would need next, while the doctor pointed out something he thought would interest the shivering boy.

Suddenly realizing that he might be late for an urgent call in another part of town, he said to Will, "You finish up here." He wiped his hands, put on his coat, gave terse instructions to clean up, sew up the incisions, and cover the corpse with the sheet. "When you have done everything, go directly home, and remember to take the specimens." Then the doctor was on his way.

Will restrained the impulse to tear out of the "squeaky old house" and run after his father as fast as his feet would carry him. He stayed to complete the job, and felt better afterwards for having overcome his terror.

Each of the boys had his "duties" when they accompanied the doctor to an operation. Will assisted by sponging and mopping the operating field, and Charlie sterilized the instruments by heating them in a charcoal stove. Charlie was also responsible for the catgut sutures and surgical needles, which he threaded with great dexterity. He was always ready with the right one when his father needed it. Listerism was still far in the future.

Will's first experience at doctoring had been the stitching up of a corpse. His younger brother unexpectedly became an anesthetist at an even earlier age. One day after school Dr. Mayo asked the boys to come along to witness and help out at an operation. He had anticipated a problem and had engaged another physician to act as anesthetist. The patient, a woman, was on the kitchen table. The boys took their positions, Will opposite his father with the sponges, Charlie tending to the sterilizing stove.

The anesthetist placed the ether cone on the patient's nose and Dr. Mayo swiftly made the incision. For some reason the assistant fell to the floor in a dead faint. The surgeon couldn't stop the operation, and he couldn't handle both the scalpel and the ether cone. Will was mopping the wound. Dr. Mayo thought quickly, then shouted to Charlie to take over. The patient was coming out of the anesthetic and showing signs of pain.

"Give her more ether, Charlie." Charlie tried to reach far enough to hold the cone over the patient's face. The doctor kicked over a cracker box for the boy to stand on: "When I raise my scalpel, give her ether; when I shake my head, stop."

Dutifully Charlie watched his father for directions, keeping one eye on the patient. When she was quiet, he stopped the ether; when she showed signs of struggling, he let the ether drip on the sponge in the cone. Confident that he had the job under control, his gaze wandered to the operation and what his father was doing.

Dr. Mayo knew it immediately. "Watch what you're doing!" The one rebuke was sufficient. Charlie stuck to his assigned task for the rest of the operation.

Throughout their growing-up years the boys were given invaluable practical experience, but the doctor saw to it that this didn't take the place of books. His library was in the dining room, lined with shelves from floor to ceiling, and often he would answer a question by taking down and handing them Gray's *Anatomy* or Paget's *Lectures on Surgical Pathology;* they were not too young to find the answers themselves, nor to read other than medical works—Darwin, Huxley, Spencer.

It was from Paget's book that the boys learned about their father's favorite source of pathological anatomy—the work of John Hunter. In time the eighteenth-century surgeon also became a source of inspiration to Will Mayo and his portrait hung in a place of honor in his office in the Mayo Clinic.

It was understood between the doctor and Mrs. Mayo that no effort would be spared to provide the boys with the best education money could buy. In fact, the entire family worked toward that end. The girls taught school and, during vacations, the boys worked in Geisinger and Newton's drugstore below Dr. Mayo's office. Mrs. Mayo cut down her husband's clothes first to fit Willie and then Charlie. Charlie's first store suit of matching coat and trousers was bought with Willie's earnings as a prescription clerk. The rest was carefully put away to add to his father's savings for Willie's education.

At nineteen Will graduated from Niles Academy in Rochester with a reasonably good background in secondary school subjects, and in a family council it was decided that he would go to Ann Arbor for his medical education. The University of Michigan had just changed its course from two to three years, and by the standards of the day was a high-ranking institution.

With a head start in anatomy and familiarity with the microscope, to say nothing of his bedside experience, it is not surprising that Will was an exemplary student, nor that he was soon selected as an assistant in dissection. The Canadian, Donald Maclean, his professor in surgery, had worked with Lister in the early days when both were house surgeons under James Syme in Edinburgh. He returned to Ontario before Lister had begun his work in antiseptic surgery, so he had no direct contact with the carbolic acid spray. He did introduce its use when he was called to fill the chair at Michigan in the seventies, but had to give it up because he was sensitive to the acid. As a result Will Mayo did not have full advantage of the new method that was beginning to revolutionize surgery in the United States.

In 1883, Will returned to Rochester and took his place alongside his father in a mutual medical practice. The formal partnership was announced in the Rochester newspaper.

A prominent citizen congratulated the tall, slender twenty-two-year-old on his medical degree, venturing the guess that now he was a full-fledged doctor, he would probably be settling in some metropolis like Chicago, or even New York. To this Will was supposed to have replied: "No, I intend to stay in Rochester and become the most famous surgeon in the world."

Two years later it was Charlie's turn, and thinking ahead to the time when his younger son would become the third partner, Dr. Mayo chose Chicago Medical College for him "because there he would get a different viewpoint."

Chicago offered a three-year course with an optional fourth year, laboratories, science courses, and a fine faculty. In addition, the students had a wide choice of clinics in Rush Medical College and any hospital in the city. Charles took full advantage of the clinical facilities at Rush, where the outstanding surgeons Nicholas Senn and Christian Fenger worked.

Fenger, a native of Copenhagen, had been educated in Europe and studied both in Heidelberg and in Vienna, under Theodor Billroth, the celebrated stomach surgeon. Senn, Swiss-born, raised in Wisconsin, had completed his medical education in German clinics. On his return, he studied under Fenger and became one of the outstanding American surgeons of his day. These men were fully indoctrinated in Listerian techniques, and from them Charles learned the new method.

He was graduated in 1888, receiving his degree after furnishing the required certificate attesting to his character. His father wrote: "To whom it may concern: This is to certify that Chas. H. Mayo is over 21 years of age and is of good moral character. W. W. Mayo."

Coming into an established practice, especially one such as

Dr. Mayo had built up in Southcentral Minnesota, had its advantages, but the boys soon found out that they had to prove themselves. When a call came in from an outlying section, the "old doctor," as he more and more came to be known, would send Will. After one look at his youthful face the farmer would send him back, saying that he meant *the* Dr. Mayo. On one occasion Dr. Mayo sent his son back four times before the patient finally agreed to have him, and then only because the "old doctor" assured him that the boy was really a doctor.

When it came Charlie's turn to be on his own, he had the same difficulties during what the boys called the "toe-in-the-door" days, and for a while he grew whiskers to make himself look older. He said later that the patients "would talk through a crack in the door, and I would put my foot in it so they couldn't close it, and would explain that Father was busy or called away." Then if he got the chance to make an examination, he would use every instrument in his bag to impress the patient, not realizing, according to Charlie, that his father would have made the diagnosis with one keen look of his experienced eye.

In August of the year Will became a doctor, Rochester was hit by a disaster that, through the efforts of the Mayos, was turned into an eventual boon, making that modest community one of the great medical centers of the world.

Dr. Will Mayo and Charlie were driving out to the slaughterhouse on the northern outskirts of the town, to pick up some eyes that Dr. Will wanted to dissect prior to an operation. With the suddenness characteristic of those western storms, a tornado swept the city. The young men raced the mare onto solid ground just before the twister lifted the bridge over the Zumbro River, which they were the last to cross. Grain elevators toppled, homes were lifted from their foundations, freight cars were derailed, farm buildings and city shops alike were battered and laid flat. Hundreds of families were homeless, twenty-two people were dead, and several hundred had been injured.

The city was completely unprepared. There was no hospital and not a single trained nurse in the entire area. The two Mayos and a few other doctors were faced with the colossal task of treating the injured.

As soon as the storm passed, Dr. Mayo and his sons, who had miraculously escaped with only damage to their carriage, rushed to the center of the town to help out. Some of the victims were carried to private homes, others into nearby doctors' offices. Dr. Mayo took the leadership in organizing effective relief for the helpless and panic-stricken community. He ordered that Rommel's Dance Hall be opened to serve as a temporary hospital, sent every able-bodied person to fetch beds, cots, bedding, and blankets from their homes, and enlisted the women as nurses. While the injured were being taken to the shelter, Dr. Mayo and his sons gave attention to those in need of immediate care. They performed emergency operations, set broken bones, stitched wounds, and even amputated with the desperate efficiency called for by a disaster. *Post facto*, the City Council met in emergency session and placed Dr. Mayo in charge of all physicians.

Among the volunteers in this work of mercy were the Franciscan nuns from the Rochester convent of Our Lady of Lourdes. One morning, while Dr. Mayo was making his rounds in the dance hall, Mother Superior Mary Alfred approached him with a startling proposal: "Rochester should have a hospital!"

"Yes, it would be a lot easier to take care of such an emergency as this, but hospitals are costly affairs to build and maintain," the doctor patiently explained. Where would the money come from in such a small city?

But the Mother Superior countered his objections: if Dr. Mayo would be willing to take charge of a hospital, the sisters of St. Francis would raise the money to build one.

How could he make such a promise? He was nearing his sixty-fifth birthday and who knew how many more years were left him for active work? But Mother Mary Alfred would not be budged, and he felt he could not let her down with a flat "no." He said he would need a little time to consider her proposal, and maybe something could come of it.

Once the idea was implanted, it began to take root. Why *not* a hospital in Rochester? During the next four years, working and sacrificing, with the doctor's encouragement, the sisters saved enough money for the building. With the fund assured, Dr. Mayo chose a site, just west of the city limits. Then he and Dr. Will drew up the plans, traveling to Chicago and eastern cities to learn how to construct a hospital.

In two more years St. Mary's Hospital was a reality.

Meanwhile, Charlie had gone off to Chicago, and Dr. Will was making a name for himself as a surgeon. He married Hattie Damon, the daughter of a Rochester jeweler and watchmaker, and after the wedding they left for New York, where the doctor combined his honeymoon with a postgraduate course at the Polyclinic Postgraduate Medical School. When Charlie graduated he too enrolled for a special course in the same hospital.

The new hospital was opened in the fall of 1889, with the three Mayos ready to staff it, although "we were a green crew

Mrs. William J. Mayo

and we knew it," as Dr. Will said. The three-story building was ready to accommodate forty patients in three wards. On the day it opened thirteen patients were admitted. Six Franciscan sisters made up its nursing staff.

Even by the standards of today's most modest hospitals, St. Mary's fell far short in its physical facilities. There was no elevator, so that the patients had to be carried up the stairs. It was lighted by kerosene lamps, which the nurses also carried to light their way on their night rounds on the wards. Water was piped from the city main into a reservoir in the basement, but from there it had to be pumped by hand. The primitive sewage system is best left undescribed. Other than the beds, there was practically no furniture, and the operating table devised by Dr. Charlie was a true makeshift. There was no telephone or hall loudspeaker and when a doctor had to be called in an emergency, one of the sisters searched him out on foot.

For all its meager facilities, the hospital was an immediate success. By the end of the first year three hundred patients had passed through its ward and received the ministrations of its brilliant young physicians and surgeons. Only two per cent of their surgical patients had died. It was an unprecedented record, but St. Mary's was a new type of hospital.

From the very beginning the Mayos and the sisters agreed on a policy of providing the same care for all patients. It would not be a "charity" hospital supported by public funds, as were the hospitals in the larger cities. Those who could not pay would be admitted free, and those who could afford it would pay as private patients, but all would be treated alike. The wisdom of this entirely new policy in hospital management was borne out the very first year: without private or public endowment St. Mary's was able to pay for itself out of patient's fees. This policy of equal treatment for all and payment according to ability continues to this day in the world-famous Mayo Clinic.

Once, early in Dr. Will's career, his father said proudly: "Yes, that boy will make a great surgeon; he's going to make his mark in the world."

But in the 1890's, future doctors went to school to become general practitioners. If later on they became exclusively surgeons, it was only because during many years of everyday practice they became especially skillful at operating. Like the others, the Mayo brothers had their full share of treating bellyaches, measles, whooping cough, bladder trouble, croup, typhoid fever, and of bringing babies into the world. They examined and prescribed for patients in the office, and rode out to see them in their homes. Now and then came a chance to operate, but mostly they were only assistants to the "old doctor."

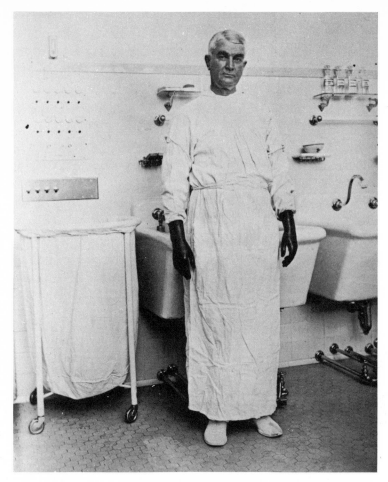

Dr. William J. Mayo

But one day Dr. Mayo was in St. Paul on a consultation and failed to show up for a scheduled ovariotomy. Dr. Will said he would do the operation if the patient was willing. She was. He removed the tumor — it filled the washtub that received it — and the group of doctors who had come to see the "old doctor" perform the operation were deeply impressed with the younger man's skill.

This was one operation Dr. Mayo thought his son had not yet grown up to, and Will was worried about what his father would say. He went down to meet the train, and hesitantly broke the news. At first his father was stunned, but almost at once he knew that the corner was turned. His son had come of age as a surgeon.

The opening of St. Mary's Hospital gave the Mayo brothers a rare opportunity to develop as surgeons. Since they had neither predecessors nor superiors in the new hospital, they had a free hand to try new methods in surgery. For a while they used the wet antiseptic method, dousing the patient, the air, and themselves with carbolic acid. But as soon as this was proved unnecessary, they adopted the newer aseptic techniques, and were among the first to buy a portable sterilizer. At this time the old doctor was seventy years old and neither willing nor able to learn new tricks, but his derision of the younger generation's innovations was good-natured, and he didn't interfere.

At the beginning of the partnership, the brothers worked as a team, taking turns at being assistant to the other, the father

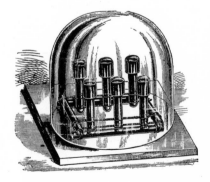

"Hat box" in which many vessels could be sterilized at once by a uniformly diffused heat of 300° F

frequently giving the anesthetic. No case was exclusively Will's or Charlie's, they were all *theirs*. Together they planned the procedures and met all emergencies. After every operation they examined specimens under the microscope, talked over their failures and successes, and decided on ways of making improvements. They had decided early that one of them always had to be on hand and that they would take turns away to study or report their work at meetings. They would also try their hands at any type of operation, but soon Will was doing most of the abdominal and pelvic surgery, and Charlie was operating on eyes, ears, noses, and throats, the brain and nerves, the bones and joints, and especially on the thyroid gland.

Will insisted that this was because Charlie was his superior: "I was driven to cover by a better surgeon. Charlie drove me down and down until I reached the belly." Actually, it was mostly a matter of time: abdominal surgery came first, and the older brother got his start in this field before Charlie developed his skill on other parts of the body.

Dr. Will had already learned gynecological surgery from his father. Then he struck out on his own in what was then a brand new field — removal of the appendix. Until the 90's, appendicitis, then called "perityphlitis," was treated with opium, calomel (mercurous chloride), castor oil, or just by waiting. Only as a last resort was surgery done, usually too late, after rupture of the appendix and the setting in of peritonitis. Since the mortality was high, appendectomy had a bad reputation, and the older surgeons feared the operation.

A bitter battle raged over the question, especially in the Middle West, the younger surgeons insisting on early recognition and operation "in time," the more conservative doctors holding to the "wait and see" approach. The Mayos steered a middle course, operating when they were sure of the diagnosis and only when it seemed reasonably safe. Always abreast of the newest developments, they adopted the treatment of a leading Chicago surgeon. They removed the appendix, preferably before it was ruptured, but if infection already had set in, they used various medical measures to carry the patient through the acute stage until it was safe to operate. As a result they were able to reduce the mortality. Their original caution and their increasing confidence are shown by the number of operations: 186 in 1900, over a thousand in 1905.

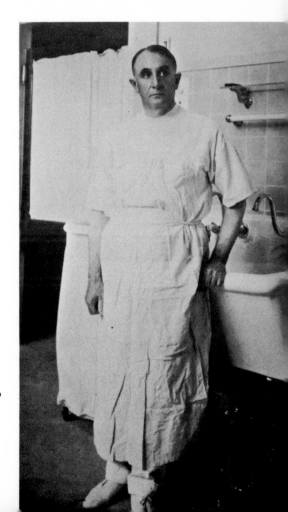

Dr. Charles H. Mayo

The Mayos were also among the first to introduce the exploratory operation. If a diagnosis could not otherwise be made, they opened the abdomen to find the cause. In this way they did their first operation for gallstones in a man who had suffered from abdominal pain for years, with no one suspecting the cause. Many other operations on the gallbladder followed, and the newspapers reported on the number of stones removed: "The number is known to be about three thousand . . . bacteriologist . . . spent all one day counting them. The woman still lives and is sure to recover."

Then came operations to remove the gallbladder and reroute the bile through new channels, the cutting out of hernias, the removal of chicken bones, coins, and safety pins caught in the esophagus, by incising the stomach or cutting through the trachea, operations to connect the upper part of the stomach with the intestine, and to remove bleeding ulcers and patch up the holes. By 1905 Dr. Will was the foremost stomach surgeon in America.

Meanwhile Dr. Charlie was performing delicate operations on the eye and cutting out tonsils and adenoids with instruments he himself invented. One of his early triumphs was the saving of a man's leg which, before his time, would have been amputated. He opened the suppurating knee joint, scraped it, and drained it of pus. After the operation, the man dragged his leg a little, but this was certainly much better than losing it.

Dr. Charlie devised a simple way of removing a foot-long section of swollen, ulcerated vein with several small incisions instead of one long slit, saving both time and extensive repair. Using a Munich surgeon's technique that had gone unrecognized for two decades, he grafted a five-inch square of skin in one operation.

Then one day a sixty-year-old farmer walked into the

office with a swelling in his neck that pushed his head back and hung down on his chest. It was the biggest thyroid the Mayos had ever seen in a geographical area where goiter was as common as bunions or baldness. The goitrous thyroid was choking the man and something had to be done soon. The usual iodine injections only made the condition more critical.

The brothers went into consultation, discussed the known risk of severe bleeding, and decided they had to operate anyhow. They put Mr. Strain on the table, gave him only a little ether (too much would have killed him), made the incision, and scooped out the tumor with their hands. As they had feared, tying off the larger blood vessels was not enough to stop the hemorrhaging, but then they remembered a device used by their father. They stuffed the wound with a sponge soaked in turpentine and sewed up the incision, bandaging it as tightly as they dared. After a few days they opened the incision and removed the sponge.

Mr. Strain lived for many years afterward, a walking testimonial to the skill of the Mayo brothers. This was the beginning of Dr. Charlie's rise to fame as a thyroid surgeon. He worked hard to improve his technique, and by 1904 he had performed sixty-eight operations of the same type, with only two deaths. By 1908, he had one thousand operations for goiter on his score board, and had earned an undisputed place as one of three leading thyroid surgeons in the United States.

People often asked who was the better of the two Mayo surgeons. To this Dr. Halsted, a contemporary "great" from Baltimore answered: "Dr. Will is a wonderful surgeon, Dr. Charlie is a surgical wonder."

News of the Mayos' successes spread far beyond the limits of Rochester. From neighboring towns and from places as far west as the new frontier in the Dakota Territory, people began to bring the "hopeless" and "incurables." The brothers never flinched at any previously untried operation if a life was at stake: the greater the difficulties of a puzzling case, the more daring they were. One or the other would travel to Chicago, New York, or even Europe to witness the work of other surgeons, or they invited them to Rochester for lectures and demonstrations. Dr. Will once went to Australia to see a particular type of incision. If a technique had not yet been developed, they worked out their own. If the proper instrument was unavailable, Dr. Charlie made one.

The Rochester papers frequently reported the Mayos' surgical feats as front-page news: Dr. Charlie repaired the mangled hand of a farmer and the man has full use of it; Dr. Will saved the life of a young girl who was suffocating from croup by inserting a tube into her trachea; the brothers removed an ovarian tumor weighing forty pounds and the patient is recovering. These reports brought other surgeons to Rochester to see how the Mayos did it, and many told how they were overwhelmed by the variety of techniques and the different procedures used.

Until 1903 the brothers did all the surgery at St. Mary's, the "old doctor" sometimes acting as anesthetist. Although retired from surgery, he took an active part in policy-making for the hospital and was still called in for consultation in medical matters. And he was not too old to continue his interest in local politics.

The Mayos' private practice flourished and the hospital received more and more applications. They invited outside physicians to use its facilities or to join the staff. In 1894 they engaged their first intern, Dr. Christopher Graham, whose sister Dr. Charlie had married. Gradually other assistants came.

Mrs. Charles H. Mayo

For a young doctor there was no better training than working under the Mayos. They imparted their knowledge freely and encouraged their assistants in the pursuit of specialties. Their influence extended far beyond Minnesota through the hundreds of articles they wrote about surgery. They were invited everywhere to read papers, and were elected members and officers of a variety of medical and surgical societies. Dr. Will was elected in 1905, and Dr. Charlie in 1916 to the presidency of the American Medical Association, the highest honor "within the power of the medical profession to bestow."

Dr. Will and Dr. Charlie, the inseparable "surgical twins," entered upon their careers when surgery was first coming into its own. With the conquest of two main obstacles — operative pain and infection — surgeons in many countries undertook operations that no one had dared to attempt before. The field was wide open for young men of skill, vision, and courage, and the Mayos had all of these attributes. They had been raised on the best that the old school offered, without being shackled by outmoded habits and practices. When asked to what they owed their success, Dr. Charlie often said, "The biggest thing Will and I ever did was to pick the father and mother we had."

Unlike their father, the Mayo brothers were financially successful from the start. Their practice was so enormous that even though they did their share of free work, and charged only the customary fees, they accumulated a sizeable fortune. The two families lived well, in a style suited to leading citizens of Rochester, but without pretentiousness. When Harvey Cushing visited the Mayos in 1908, he wrote: "Both . . . are charming fellows and lead a simple life and in a simple community." But at least eight or nine years earlier, the Mayos had realized they were making more money than they needed.

The brothers maintained a joint bank account, and one day Dr. Will received quite a jolt when he took a look at the balance. The two sat down for a serious talk, and Will asked, "What should we do with all the money that's flowing in, Charlie?"

That thought never worried their father, when he used to say to Charlie, whose job it was to post his bills, "Those are poor folk; don't put them in the book."

Still, though they followed the same practice with their own patients, the bank account was mounting to a frightening sum.

"We ought to extend the 'no charge' policy to doctors, nurses, ministers, teachers, missionaries, and all those state workers on small salaries," Dr. Will proposed. "Everyone should get the same kind of care whether he can pay or not."

"Should we lower our fees?" the younger brother asked.

"No, that would get us into trouble with other doctors," said Dr. Will, the more adept in economic matters.

"This money that's piling up," said Charlie, "came from the sick. Why shouldn't it be used to help the sick?"

As they continued talking, they decided to increase their facilities, make it possible for their assistants to travel and improve themselves, then raise the quality of their practice with the best of innovations.

But their most important decision was to set aside one of every two dollars they earned. They would turn this money over to some smart lawyer who knew how to invest it in the increasingly profitable businesses of lumber, mining, railroads, and construction materials. Then the income could be put to good use, particularly in helping more young people to become doctors, good doctors to serve the sick ever better.

The realization of this dream was still in the future, but the beginning was definitely settled on: in such matters the brothers were of one mind.

For years to come Mr. Burt W. Eaton, a Rochester lawyer, would take "his half for the investment account," which grew astonishingly in those days of rapid economic expansion, and now and then would give them an accounting.

In the meantime the hospital too was growing and its facilities were being improved. New wings were added, more wards opened, and additional operating rooms constructed. The brothers established laboratories, instituted new experimental work, and acquired the latest equipment.

The reputation of the Mayos was on its way to becoming world-wide during the first decade of the twentieth century. As more and more patients flocked to Rochester from every state in the Union and from foreign lands, it became impossible for the brothers to see them all personally for diagnosis. To solve this problem they thought up a brand new idea in private medical practice.

They would establish a clinic where each patient would be seen by a number of specialists and examined by every conceivable diagnostic technique. The final diagnosis would be based on the collective opinion of the best trained minds in each field, then the treatment prescribed. If surgery was recommended, the brothers would do the operating. Thus, the Mayo Clinic — the first of its kind to offer private group practice — came into being.

The Clinic building was a four-story brick structure, located on the site of Dr. Mayo's original home in Rochester, where Dr. Charlie was born. It opened its doors in 1913. Although everyone, including the Mayos, thought they might have overreached themselves in building offices and laboratories for 15,000 patients a year, by the end of the first year 25,000 had been examined and treated.

Today the "Clinic in the Cornfields" occupies a skyscraper building where 2,500 patients *daily* seek medical advice.

The "old doctor," who never lost his interest in medical affairs, was in on the planning of the Clinic and visited the hospital every day. When well along in his eighties, he went around the world twice, taking in the foreign clinics and hospitals. At the age of ninety he was still hearty, enjoying fine horses and making a hobby of farm machinery. In 1911, after three operations following an accident in which he caught his arm in a piece of machinery, he died at the age of ninety-two. The entire city of Rochester went into mourning, and a bronze statue was erected in Mayo Park with funds contributed by the citizenry. Inscribed on the monument are these words by his son William: PIONEER: PHYSICIAN-CITIZEN: A MAN OF HOPE AND FORWARD-LOOKING MIND.

Mrs. Mayo was present at the unveiling ceremony, looking on from a wheel chair. A few months later she too quietly passed away.

———

By 1915, the sums set aside by the Mayos each year for investment added up to a million and a half dollars. This was the money they had planned as young men to turn back for the welfare of the sick, and they were now ready to use it.

With the Board of Trustees of the University of Minnesota assisting in the planning, they established the Mayo Foundation for Medical Education and Research. Dr. Will and Dr. Charlie endowed the Foundation by transferring the fund to three trustees, one of whom was Mr. Eaton.

Mayo Clinic buildings. The one in foreground was built in 1955. The skyscraper in background was built in 1929

In essence the plan provided for fellowships for post-graduate work in Rochester to recent medical graduates sponsored and accredited by the university. The plan was acclaimed in the entire country's press as one of the "wonder stories of America" and "a fitting climax to . . . a distinctively American career," but there also were many who noisily opposed it.

Some were against the affiliation of a state institution with a "private fund"; others directed their attacks against the Mayos personally: it would bring them a lot of advertising, they would turn their charity cases over to the students while themselves collecting fat fees from private patients, and the state would end up by paying the freight.

With dignity and restraint the Mayo brothers met the vilification with straightforward reasons for their plan. Said Dr. Will: "If we wanted money, we have it. That can't be the reason for our offer. We want the money to go back to the people, from whom it came, and we think we can best give it back to them through medical education. . . . This foundation, its fund . . . are the contributions of the sick of this generation to prevent the sickness and suffering in the next and following generations. . . . "

The storm finally subsided, and the Mayo Foundation continues to this day to train each year up to two hundred young doctors in surgery and other fields of medicine.

Assured of the success of their magnificent contribution to the advancement of medical science, the Mayo brothers continued to work in the institutions their genius and work had created.

In 1939, the two surgeons, inseparable in their life work, died less than two months apart, Dr. Charlie at 74 from pneumonia, Dr. Will's life, at 78, just ebbing away from the shock of the loss of his brother.

As part of the obituary, the great surgeon Harvey Cushing, who himself died some weeks after Dr. Will, wrote:

"There was nothing mysterious or supernatural about this twentieth-century Lourdes at whose doors incredible numbers of the lame, halt, and blind have for years been daily delivered from the ends of the earth. Nothing supernatural — unless possibly the flawless, life-long devotion of two brothers for one another be so regarded. . . .

" . . . they very much preferred their own countryside with its comparatively simple life, despite the ever-increasing responsibilities and laborious routine of their professional work. They felt only an amused pity for those who thought they were wasting their talents in a small town and who ventured to offer them positions elsewhere of supposedly wider influence."

CHAPTER TWELVE

Explorers of the Brain

Before successful surgery could be undertaken on the brain, much exploration needed to be done. In the 1860's there was still much guessing and little knowledge about the brain. Was the brain, like the liver, one organ, the same in every part, or was it composed of many different parts, each with its own function? This was only one of the questions that required an answer. Now that the physiologist could use the tools — anesthesia and asepsis — just made available to the surgeon, he was ready to explore the brain in animals.

If parts were removed piece by piece from the foremost part of the brain of a pigeon, the bird recovered each time without missing the lost part. Only when the brain was completely gone would the pigeon stop flying, seeing, and feeding itself.

The idea of the unity of function of all parts of the brain made sense when somewhat similar results were obtained in experiments with frogs, cats, and dogs. The removal of portions of the brain in succession did not seem to deprive the animal of one or another special function. As long as the operation was done in stages, and the animals were kept in the care of a laboratory, they survived and showed no loss. They could walk, crawl, jump, swim, eat, and croak or bark according to their nature. The obvious conclusion was that the brain was one organ, and if enough of it was left intact, every part must work like every other.

A chance observation in a patient by a French neurosurgeon brought this idea into question. In 1861, Pierre Paul Broca examined the brain of a dead woman who had lost her power of speech several years before she died. He noticed that a well-defined area in the left frontal lobe of the brain was clearly deteriorated. He decided that his patient's loss of speech had been caused by the softening of this part of her brain, and concluded that the left frontal lobe normally controlled speech or the ability to form words. He called this area (the left side in right-handed persons) the speech center. In fact, he went on to say that the brain was probably made up of many centers, each governing some special function. There must be centers for motion, seeing, hearing, touching and so on, Broca argued.

As it happened, he could not prove his idea of a speech center by systematic experiments in animals, since only man can speak. And since the earlier experiments in animals seemed to point against the existence of specialized parts in the brain, Broca's idea was largely ignored. The few who paid any attention to it were violently opposed to such a notion.

Within a very few years a young English doctor, working in a small hospital in London, observed something that put him on Broca's track.

John Hughlings Jackson was the son of Samuel Jackson who farmed a small parcel of land near the village of Green Hammerton a few miles northeast of York. The boy was born in 1835 into a family of four other children. One of his brothers had gone to New Zealand and had fought so well for England against the Maori that the government had given him a large grant of land. He was later elected to the House of Representatives.

Hughlings, as he came to be called, attended the village school at Green Hammerton and neighboring secondary schools which he later said did him "little harm from over-education." As a youth he was apprenticed to a Mr. Anderson who lectured to about a dozen students in the medical school at York. From York, Jackson went to St. Bartholomew's Hospital in London and had the good fortune to study under Sir James Paget, the distinguished surgeon, pathologist, and authority on bone diseases.

When he returned to York, Jackson became house surgeon in the Dispensary where Thomas Laycock, a brilliant teacher, stimulated the young student's interest in mental disease. Jackson joined a medical club in which each member, whenever possible, arranged for a post-mortem examination and invited his fellow members to attend.

In 1859 Jackson received an appointment as physician to the Metropolitan Free Hospital and Lecturer on Pathology at the London Hospital. From then until the end of his life, teaching was a major interest, giving him the opportunity he wanted to "philosophize" in medicine and to develop a theory of nervous diseases, based on evolutionary levels of the nervous system.

Jackson lived at a time when some of the best minds in the medical profession devoted their attention to questions of neurology and nervous diseases. In the year that Jackson came to London, a new kind of hospital was founded — The National Hospital for the Paralyzed and Epileptic — and in 1862 Jackson was invited to join it as assistant physician.

Jackson noted that his patients who were paralyzed on the right side frequently lost their power of speech. Autopsy revealed that the paralysis was connected with a cerebral hemorrhage, and the interesting thing was that the paralyzed side was opposite to the side of the brain where he found the blood clot. The fact that speech loss usually accompanied a right-sided paralysis gave added weight to Broca's conclusion that the center for speech was in the left half of the brain.

Jackson was neither a surgeon nor an experimenter, but he had a genius for observing symptoms and connecting them up with the possible cause in a diseased brain. His acuteness in observing clinical facts to the last detail led him to certain far-reaching conclusions about the functioning of the brain which are still held today. In his own day he was nicknamed "The Sage," for his profoundly correct analysis of the workings of the most complicated organ in the body.

He is best known for his investigation of one type of epilepsy, named after him, which may be cured by surgery, because it is caused by localized damage to the brain. In these cases he noticed that the epileptic fit began with a spasm on one side, in which the parts of the body became involved according to a regular pattern of violent twitches: first the index finger, next the hand, then the whole arm, then the face, and then the leg became convulsed. This order of involvement, he reasoned, could be explained by the fact that the parts having the most precise and varied movements were the most affected by the pressure of the tumor. The smaller muscles of the hand, whose movements were more delicate, were represented by a larger area in the brain than were the bigger muscles of the leg. This idea that a particular part of the brain governed the movements of a specific part of the body was provocative at that time, and it was later to become of the first importance for surgery of brain tumors.

Hughlings Jackson, from a painting by Lance Calkin

By a strange irony Jackson was able to study this type of convulsion in his own family.

In 1865, after a long engagement, he married Elizabeth Dade Jackson, his first cousin. "There was nothing in the world to compare with domestic happiness," he said. But his happiness was marred by his wife's frequent convulsions, which were due to cerebral disease. Mrs. Jackson finally died after eleven years of married life. The cause of her death was a cerebral blood clot which had led to her convulsions. Today this disease is called Jacksonian epilepsy.

Without experimentation, Jackson had arrived at his theory of specific centers in the brain for movements of special muscle groups, the first definite idea of cerebral localization. His work was soon to receive confirmation. During the Prussian war on Denmark, a German doctor, Gustav Theodor Fritsch, attending a soldier with severe head wounds, noticed that when he chanced to touch certain parts of the exposed brain, twitching movements occurred in specific parts of the soldier's body on the opposite side.

Several years later this interesting observation was still on Fritsch's mind, and he decided to investigate it in animals. He joined the neurologist, Edward Hitzig, who was then working at the Berlin Physiological Institute. Together they did a series of experiments, opening the skulls of dogs and exposing the meningeal covering of the brain. They touched a "live" electric wire carrying a feeble current to one side of the brain; much to their surprise, the muscles on the other side of the dog's body twitched. The dog, anesthetized with ether, certainly could not move his legs at will, but every time they repeated this stimulation, the muscles moved.

Then they inserted pins as markers, killed the dogs, and exposed the brain. Thus they mapped the parts of the brain in the frontal area that had sparked the movement of specific muscle groups. They called this part of the brain the *motor area*, and the precise points in it the "motor centers" which started the muscles off.

The report of the Fritsch experiments reached England in 1871. The motor centers which they demonstrated in the dog were the very ones that Jackson had "guessed" had set off the sequence of convulsions in his patients. Like Jackson, Fritsch and Hitzig advanced the idea that the brain was not, like the liver or kidney, a single organ. Rather, it was com-

posed of a number of functional centers each with a specialized type of activity.

In the meantime, Broca continued to perform autopsies on
the skulls of patients who had suffered from paralysis, severe
headaches, or occasional loss of consciousness during convulsions. In one particular case he found a sizeable tumor which,
because enclosed in a capsule, could easily be separated from
the underlying brain tissue. This patient had been paralyzed
on the opposite side and had suffered severe headaches. It
was now within the realm of possibility that some patients
could be relieved of these disabling symptoms if the skull
were trephined with a circular saw, and the tumor removed
surgically. The knowledge that the trouble spot in the brain
could be located from the symptoms was a distinct possibility.
However, it was some time before the idea of localization in
the higher centers of the brain was accepted.

Physiologists were still arguing about whether the brain
was a single or multiple organ, and a decade after Fritsch's
and Hitzig's experiments the controversy was still raging.
Its principals were in London and in Berlin.

In Germany, Friedrich Goltz had for a number of years
experimented with the nervous system of frogs. After removing the brain, he found that when left alone the frog lay
motionless on the board and did not go after food. But if
Goltz struck the board with his fist, the frog twitched; when
he dipped its legs into warm water, or put a drop of acid on
the skin, the legs were drawn up; if he stroked its belly, it
croaked, and if he dropped it into a bowl of water, it swam.
He concluded that the brain was not needed for these functions, and that the rest of the frog's system served as a chain
of reflex centers. By proper stimulation Goltz could reproduce its predictable reflex behavior.

Goltz was certainly correct in his conclusions, as any biology student will recognize from these same familiar experiments on frogs. From frogs, Goltz went on to dogs. By painstaking experiments in which he must have lost a great many, he succeeded in turning one dog into a completely reflex animal. In successive operations, the dog's brain was removed. It could still walk, snarl, bark, perk up its ears at a noise, and take food that was held up to its nose. Although it could do all of these things, it had lost its memory, the ability to learn, and other signs of intelligent behavior. An "imbecile," it still was able to respond somewhat like a reflex frog to certain stimuli. The animal received the best of care and lived for eighteen months. How could there be controlling centers for these functions in the brain, when the debrained dog still retained the ability to walk or even jump? Goltz argued. He was a careful experimenter, and his results seemed to be a flat contradiction to the views of Broca, Jackson, Fritsch, and Hitzig.

In England, David Ferrier, a doctor and lecturer in physiology, undertook his own exploration of the brain which eventually led him to an open clash with the Goltz supporters.

———

David Ferrier, the son of a small businessman, was born in Aberdeen, Scotland in 1843. He attended the schools in his native city, distinguishing himself as a pupil. At the age of seventeen he achieved first place in a competition for a scholarship to the University of Aberdeen where he enrolled as an arts student. In 1863 he received the Master of Arts degree with honors in classics and philosophy. He was also awarded the Ferguson scholarship which was open to the graduates of all four Scottish universities. This enabled him to go on to Edinburgh as a medical student. In three years he received his Bachelor of Medicine degree. Like Hughlings Jackson, he had studied under Thomas Laycock, who by this time had left the York Dispensary and gone on to Edinburgh as Professor of Practical Medicine. As an assistant to Laycock, Ferrier coached his students for a while after graduation, but he didn't find this work stimulating enough to hold him there.

He took a job as an assistant to a Dr. Image of Bury St. Edmunds, about sixty miles northeast of London. While he had some duties as helper to the general practitioner, he spent most of the time in the congenial setting of Dr. Image's lovely garden investigating the brains of various animals. His research was fruitful, in that he contributed to the anatomy of several parts of the brain stem. He presented his results in the form of a thesis, for which he was granted the M. D. degree and a gold medal besides.

In 1870 he received an appointment as Lecturer in Physiology at the Medical School of Middlesex Hospital in London, and after one year also filled a similar post in the Medical School of King's College. Soon he succeeded the famous Dr. Guy in the Chair of Forensic Medicine. In these early years in London he came to know Hughlings Jackson well, and followed his work on the mechanism of epilepsy. His interest was definitely in the direction of nervous diseases.

One evening at a friend's house, when the conversation turned to the work of Fritsch and Hitzig, Ferrier decided to pursue his own systematic work of exploring the brain's surface layer, the cortex. He planned to carry his investigation from the lowest to the highest vertebrate animals, on the hunch that what might be true in the frog was not necessarily duplicated in the higher animals. The Royal Society awarded him a grant to carry this work up to the apes, which were nearer to man than was the dog.

His first reports on this work began to flow from his pen in 1873 from the West Riding Asylum, a mental hospital where his friend Dr. Wakefield provided him with research facilities, and furnished him with fowls, guinea pigs, rabbits, cats, and dogs. An experimenter and comparative anatomist by his earlier training, Ferrier was in his element among this diversity of animal species. Going from his researches to his classes, he brought to his students the results of his findings.

"Many persons, mocking, ask: What has mind to do with brain-substance, white or grey? Can any facts or laws regarding the spirit of man be gained through a scrutiny of nerve-fibres and nerve-cells?" he asked categorically, and answered: "We may possibly unlock the secrets of the structure, may compel the cells and fibres to disclose their meaning and purpose."

He set about testing the theory of Hughlings Jackson that localized one-sided epilepsies are caused by irritative "discharging" lesions of the grey matter of the cerebral hemispheres. Extending the work of Fritsch and Hitzig to monkeys and apes, he made an important advance. While the Germans had used a galvanic or constant current, he applied a faradic or interrupted current which enabled him to produce more precise and fleeting twitching movements. Besides, this type of current allowed him to study these easily repeated movements without damage to the brain tissue.

In this way he was able to reproduce in animals the pattern of twitches in spreading sequence that Jackson had so carefully studied in human epileptics. Like an explorer, he mapped the parts he localized in his explorations. Not only did he discover that the motor area started the muscles off, but also he found that a small part of that area would make one set of muscles move, but not another. The top of the brain, when stimulated, made the toes and feet wiggle. The next section down made the legs twitch, while the next lower one moved muscles of the back. Then came the part for the arms, then the face. His chart was like an orderly map.

At will, he could now stimulate one area or another of the brain and get the different parts of the body to move. He also found that it was always the *right* side of the brain that controlled the *left* side of the body.

Extending his exploration to other parts of the cortex, he discovered sensory as well as motor centers. The brain did more than just start muscles off. Ferrier now found that it also had special parts for seeing, hearing, and feeling. The eyes, the ears, and the nerves in the skin connected up with a special central switch in the brain. The brain, therefore, was an organ of many centers. In this he broke new ground. "A scientific phrenology is regarded as possible," he wrote.

Ferrier was now ready to announce to the entire medical world his scheme of localization of function in the cortex. The opportunity came in 1881 when an International Medical Congress met in London.

The importance of the occasion was marked by the presence of royalty. The Prince of Wales opened the historic meeting in St. James Hall, and the German Crown Prince was a guest. Among the medical notables were Sir Joseph Lister, Hughlings Jackson, Stephen Paget, Louis Pasteur, Jean Martin Charcot, the renowned French neurologist, Rudolf Virchow, the German pathologist, and scores of others from all parts of the world.

While the Congress as a whole was open to thousands of physicians, the physiological section, where the battle over the functions of the brain would begin, was restricted to an invited audience. A special crisis in the advancement of biological science threatened the meeting. The anti-vivisectionists in England were agitating for a strict law against the use of animals for experiments. The battle had been raging for a number of years, spearheaded by vegetarians, homeopaths, and ignorant persons who would spare the dog, no matter what the loss to man. They had won a partial victory in 1876 when a law was passed limiting the use of animals to scientists under special license. But the anti-vivisectionists, who didn't care a fig about the foxes and deer killed in the hunt, seized every opportunity to whip up sentiment against *all* animal experimentation.

Advance publicity for the meeting indicated that Professor Goltz was bringing a mutilated dog to demonstrate at the Congress. Indeed, he was carrying his precious debrained animal as personal baggage; with him came a special attendant who looked after the dog that was specially sensitive to cold and other environmental conditions. The faddist animal lovers were fuming, but there was nothing they could do about a foreigner, who after all was not subject to British laws.

The other principal in this heated contest over a fundamental question was Professor Ferrier, who would be the chief target of the enemies of vivisection. His supporters feared that under the restrictions of the law he would be unable to demonstrate his experiments freely. The atmosphere was therefore doubly tense as Dr. Michael Foster, the chairman of the meeting, rose to open the session. There was no need for him to call the audience to attention.

All present recognized that this was a great moment in the history of medical science. The chairman announced the well-known names of the contestants: Professors Goltz and

Ferrier. He explained that after each of them presented his verbal arguments, the audience would repair to a laboratory in King's College, where the animals would be demonstrated. The animals would then be killed and autopsies performed for the assembled to witness.

The stocky round-headed Prussian stepped forward on the platform, fully confident that he had already won his case. What if Fritsch and Hitzig had seen twitching muscles when they stimulated the brain? He could produce the same twitchings by stimulating the motor nerves in the limbs and the spinal cord, and certain sensory nerves. As indeed he could. The proof was in the removal of large sections of the brain. If the animal were kept alive long enough, the temporary paralysis wore off. Apparently, after a while, what remained of the brain could take over the normal functions. This proved conclusively that the older idea of the brain functioning as a whole was correct. For his dog, deprived of both frontal lobes, still moved its limbs, tail, jaw, eyes, and ears. As a finishing thrust in this heated debate, Goltz produced from his suitcase a damaged skull, and a small portion of pickled brain. This came from a dog on which he had performed several operations without impairing its functions. Everyone could see that there was nothing left in the brain remnant of Ferrier's motor or sensory centers!

It was now time for Ferrier to present his refutation. The slight, erect Englishman, his sparse hair parted in the middle, and his large drooping mustache properly groomed, stepped up to the platform. In a genial, quiet manner he stated that he had no quarrel with Professor Goltz's results; indeed, he fully accepted his careful observations. He rejected only Professor Goltz's conclusions.

But Ferrier was bitingly critical of the crudeness of

Sir David Ferrier (1843–1928)

Goltz's experiments on the most delicate of all organs, his wholesale excision of large parts of the brain, his neglecting to control hemorrhage, and the exposure to infection which killed so many of Goltz's dogs. His own method, he said, was much more precise, using the latest method of controlling bleeding, and aseptic techniques, so that his own animals survived. The very disregard for precision in Goltz's wholesale destruction brought into doubt the absence of remnants of the motor and sensory centers. How could Goltz be sure that parts of these did not remain?

Ferrier's most telling argument, however, was that a pigeon's or even a dog's brain was quite unlike a man's brain. For this reason he had studied the ape's and monkey's brain, in which he had removed certain centers under the most careful surgical methods. The results in these higher animals were similar to what one sees in patients with damaged brains, he stated.

Later, at the demonstration, Goltz presented his debrained dog. Like a circus master, he cracked a whip and the animal cringed; he opened the cage and ordered him to walk out; the animal responded to the sound of his voice; he was clearly sensitive to light, because he avoided the rays of sunlight streaming in through the window; when blindfolded he walked right into the light. The dog withdrew from painful pricking of his skin with a pair of forceps. The audience could see for itself, Goltz declared, that though deprived of intelligent behavior, the dog had lost none of his motor or sensory functions. It could walk, see, hear, and feel. This was proof that there was nothing to this theory of localization in the brain, he concluded.

It was time for the second contestant to present the living evidence to support his theory. An animal attendant came into the room leading a large monkey. Ferrier himself stood aside as the visitors took in the scene. To doctors familiar with the gait of a one-sided paralytic, the monkey had an eerie resemblance to a patient who had suffered a "stroke." The animal was dragging one leg, and its forepaw hung limply. This was a walking imitation of a patient recovered from the first effects of a cerebral hemorrhage. In fact, as one doctor exclaimed: "It *is* a patient."

In every other way the monkey was normal: it snatched at food and ate it with obvious pleasure; it took in with interest the room crowded with strangers. It had lost neither its sight nor its intelligence. When Ferrier fired a cap pistol, the monkey jumped in terror, falling to the floor without the use of its paralyzed side. It was possessed of its senses, but it had lost the use of two of its limbs.

A second monkey, having the full use of its four limbs, was then brought in. By the same careful surgery, another part of its brain had been removed. The firing of the cap pistol which rang through the room left this monkey unperturbed. It had lost the sensory center for hearing! In all other respects it was normal.

There was little left for Ferrier to say by way of summarizing what the overwhelmed clinicians had witnessed. Only this: that further pinpointing of specific areas in the brain should have enormous importance for surgery of the brain and the treatment of diseases of this organ.

This historic Congress established the principle of specific brain centers, opening a new era for brain surgery. At the time, Hughlings Jackson and David Ferrier still had many years of active work ahead.

After the death of his wife, Dr. Jackson led the life of a lonely man, shy, and retiring from social contacts. But he continued with deep absorption to study the problems of nervous disorders. He could not be easily distracted from a problem that occupied him. One day, Sir Henry Head, a well-known neurologist, ran into him in the street. Head had just discovered how regenerated nerves slowly regain their sensitivity, and he was eager to tell Jackson about it.

"Don't bother me now, Head. I'm making some observations on my own migraine," Jackson snapped back.

Jackson made famous the National Hospital for the Paralyzed and Epileptic, and expanded the doctrines by which he sought to explain the diseases he studied there. He continued to lecture and guide his students in accurate observation. His contributions were highly valued during his lifetime, and the esteem that he had earned among his peers was shown on the occasion of the centenary of his birth in 1935.

Returning from Jackson's funeral in 1911, Ferrier commented: "Well, when I cease to take interest in things it will be time for me to go." A shrewd observer, keenly alive to men and things and a first rank scientist, he continued his work in a field which he helped to open up. He led the way for others to follow and was honored in his own day. In the year of Jackson's death, Ferrier was knighted; in 1914 he was granted an honorary Doctor of Science degree from Cambridge and elected a Laureate of the Académie de Médicin in Paris. With Jackson he was a founder of the journal *Brain*, and a president of the Neurological Society, of which he was one of the founders. He died in 1928.

While today the name of Friedrich Goltz has only obscure historical interest, those of Jackson and Ferrier live on. Modern brain surgery stands on the firm building blocks of their work.

CHAPTER THIRTEEN

The Master Brain Surgeon

While the pioneering Mayo brothers were making surgical history in the "Clinic in the Cornfields," a distinguished contemporary was breaking ground in Baltimore. In the spring of 1909, flushed with enthusiasm over his first case of a tumor of the pituitary, the little gland at the base of the brain, he wrote his father:

"It seems to me an important gland and one which is surgically accessible. I have had one clinical case — an acromegaly patient. It is quite extraordinary how he has improved — quite a brilliant affair all round. Chas. Mayo sent him down to me from Rochester and the chap walked into the clinic on his sixth day after operation when our Surgical Club was here — as much to my astonishment as to theirs. I think it is the first case in this country. . . .

"Patients have been coming — most of them with brain tumors. I think the list would interest you: Boston, Vancouver, B. C., Westchester, N. Y., Washington, D. C., Batesburg, S. C., Morristown, N. J., Bangor, Me., Louisville, Ky., Ottawa, Ont., La Crosse, Wis., a South Dakota patient [the farmer whom C. H. Mayo had sent] . . ."

This was Harvey Cushing at the age of forty.

Harvey Cushing, descendant of a long line of general practitioners, was the first surgeon in the family, and proved to be one of a handful of the world's best. His great-grandfather was a country doctor in Massachusetts, and his grandfather, Dr. Erastus Cushing, migrated from the Berkshire hills, by the Erie Canal, to what was then the Western Reserve of Connecticut. It was there, after it had become Ohio, that Harvey was born in the town of Cleveland, on April 8, 1869, the youngest of ten children of Dr. Henry Kirke Cushing and Betsey Maria Williams Cushing.

His oldest brother, William Erastus, was sixteen; then came Alice, ten, who was actually the fifth child (three other girls died in infancy); Henry, nine; Edward, seven; George, five; and Alleyne, still a toddler, to whom Harvey felt closest in their growing-up years.

Dr. Cushing was a stern father, "too much so as I remember, in his treatment of his sons. Their mother was the one to whom the boys turned for the few indulgences permitted," a friend of the family recalled. Harvey himself remembered his mother as the one "to whom I must return as we sooner or later always did with cuts or bruises or torn clothes or hurt feelings." When she wasn't mending or making their clothes, or cooking and putting up preserves, she gave the children the rudiments of their education. "Yet she never seemed to be hurried and was never known to show impatience."

For all his austerity, extreme reticence, and puritannical nature, the doctor was completely devoted to Mrs. Cushing and "kindness and tenderness itself" when Harvey suffered a fracture in an athletic event of which his father had heartily disapproved. There were times when Dr. Cushing spoke to no one in the family for days, but they forgave him, knowing that he was easily offended, overworked, and under the strain of so many sleepless nights of obstetrical work. It was only by working for forty years without a vacation that he managed to maintain and educate the seven children who grew into adulthood. If he was inordinately penurious, it is not surprising in view of the heavy responsibilities he shouldered.

The Cushing children had the enviable advantages of a large, closely knit family, brimming with affection but with never a trace of coddling. All had to share in the work of the household — cutting the grass, watering the garden, raking the paths, sweeping the walks. Like their out-grown clothes, these chores were handed down from the oldest to the youngest and assumed "with a certain pride." Loafing was not tolerated, and a sensible discipline was strictly maintained: ". . . duly spanked for our peccadillos, I think by both parents, Father's favorite weapon being the back of a hair brush on the open palm or the same on the buttocks while across his knees until we got too big for that. I'm sure it was good for us and probably hurt them the most," Harvey remembered.

Harvey had the happy childhood of any normal boy, playing shinny, tag, ducks and drakes, hare and hounds, base-ball and football; he swam, skated, collected postage stamps, coins, butterflies, and bird's eggs, and trained his dog to play the piano and to run to meet the paper-boy and bring the paper home. Extremely graceful and agile, he was an excellent dancer and excelled in tumbling and in feats of the flying rings and parallel bars in the barn gymnasium. During summer vacations he went on hiking and boating trips up the Great Lakes and loved the rugged life of camping out.

He attended the Sterling Street Grammar School and Central High School in Cleveland, graduating eleventh in the class of eighty-three students. He was class president during his senior year and was listed as giving a tumbling exhibition at the class entertainment. Perhaps if he hadn't grown up to be so famous, his early scholastic ability would have gone unnoticed. As it happened, one of his high school teachers wrote him many years later: "I saw it all twenty-seven years ago and have had the great delight of watching the materializing of my vision. You surely have become all that I hoped and dreamed you might be, and I think I placed my standard for you at the very top notch."

This same teacher firmly believed in the merits of training in manual dexterity, and so Harvey and his classmates were drilled in handling rowboats and canoes, in carpentering, wood-turning, and metal forging "like so many blacksmiths learning to strike when the iron was hot — the best possible cure for youthful indecision," Cushing himself was convinced.

In 1887, at the age of eighteen, he passed the entrance examination in Chicago and that fall entered Yale, where he shared a room with his cousin, Perry Harvey. They were not overly enthusiastic about either the rooming house or its skimping landlady: "You see I have not been here long enough to become enthusiastic about it and it is not a place to become so at first sight," he wrote home.

But if we can judge from his long and detailed letters on his courses, instructors, athletic activities, and new friends, he was before long in the full swing of college life. What he couldn't describe in words he filled in with pictures — the arrangement of his room, the crystals he saw under the microscope — giving his parents little reason to wonder how he spent his time.

One item that appeared in almost every letter to his father was an appeal for funds. At least once a month he accounted

Harvey Cushing, from a photograph taken in January 1889 when he was a sophomore at Yale

for his expenses in the greatest detail to show why he had to have more money: "I have to again send a supplication to you for money. It seems as though you sent me just a day or two ago that $40 which, in making out my accounts last night, I find to be too small to pay my board bill for $12, which comes in every other Friday. . . . I take the *News* — a daily which costs four dollars; it is almost a necessity as all the notices etc. are printed in it. I also take the *Record*, a bi-weekly for $1.50 and the *Yale Literary Magazine* for $3.00 . . ." Enclosed was an itemized expense account which included fifty cents for the "trunk to the depot," ten cents for carfare, twenty-five for breakfast, and twenty-five cents for a "chicken show."

Another bone of contention was Harvey's participation in athletics. He was playing shortstop on the freshman baseball team, and when they were scheduled to play the Harvard freshmen, he wrote home for permission to play.

The reply came: "Dear Harvey, I will try to reply to

your letter calmly, though I do feel sore and disturbed over the unhappy position you have brought us into. I carefully explained before you went to New Haven, that we were going into a partnership with mutual responsibilities and duties. I was to supply the means, and you to conduct yourself to my approval while the partnership survived. Among the conditions I insisted on, and which I understood you to assent to, were those that you would not smoke, drink or be guilty of any immoral conduct or join a College ball club or boat crew. . . ."

However, the doctor relented somewhat by adding that if the boy could not withdraw gracefully from the Harvard game, he would do no more about it, but *"that must be the end of that sort of thing absolutely and for good."*

This must have seemed a very harsh restriction for a boy with his well-built, muscular form and athletic ability, but apparently he took it without rancor. To be sure it didn't curb him completely, for he later won the prize in a tumbling exhibition, and there is a picture of him in Medical School doing a back somersault from the steps of the building, and landing on the sidewalk with a still-lit cigarette in his mouth.

Harvey's interest in science developed gradually, inspired by some of the most brilliant scientists then teaching at Yale. Among them was Professor Russell H. Chittenden, who was making important advances in a new branch — physiological chemistry. Also, his brother Edward (Ned), the only other Cushing boy to become a physician, was studying medicine at Harvard and invited him occasionally for a visit to the hospital. Harvey was impressed with the fine buildings and the men he met in the wards, but mostly he appreciated the opportunity to sit in with the other students and watch his brother operate.

He considered it a great privilege, "like private instruction," when in his junior year Professor Chittenden asked him to help in class, and wrote to his father: "It's the finest course I have had here and ever expect to have in that line of work and I would not be willing to lose any of it for the sake of college baseball which happily is not necessary." Still he was undecided on a career, even toying with the idea of using his skill in drawing to become an architect. But other influences played a part in his final decision.

In 1891 he attended a Senior Society Saturday night talk by a doctor on the history of medicine. The speaker told about the contributions of Paget, Lister, Pasteur, Virchow, and Koch, who had reported at Medical Congresses he had attended. "A man can't help congratulating himself every day for the opportunity of meeting these men on the same level, which a Senior Society here gives him," he told his father.

On his graduation from Yale the same year, Cushing decided to study medicine at Harvard. Dr. Chittenden urged him to continue at Yale, but he chose to follow in the footsteps of his brother, who by that time had finished Medical School. He may have been influenced also by the superior standing of Harvard, which it owed partly to the splendid leadership of Charles W. Eliot, President of the University since 1869.

Cushing left behind his friends of the Scroll and Key Fraternity and so many intimate and warm associations in Yale that for a time he was lost in Boston: "It seems to me I never saw so many people before who were all utter strangers and it's most depressing. . . ." His father tried to comfort him and reassure him that undoubtedly he would do as well as Ned and Will (who had gone to the law school), but added a word of guidance: "Men go astray in great numbers . . .

under the temptations of one kind and another that in-
sidiously beguile. Playing cards for money, tippling [drink-
ing], and frequenting haunts of immoral women are the three
chief ways in which young men have wrecked themselves...."

Perhaps this advice was unnecessary because the young
medical student, no longer the Yale socialite, "decided to be
a leper," and from then on medicine became his life. From
the very beginning he distinguished himself in dissection; before the first day passed both students and teachers were
impressed with his progress. He spent his Saturday afternoons
watching operations — observing every detail with borrowed
opera glasses — which he described in letters to his father: an
amputation, excision of a knee, removal of an enlarged testicle,
and "especially interesting" the extraction, from a woman's
esophagus, of false teeth she had swallowed six weeks before.

As time went on his letters became even more detailed:
his election to the Boylston Society, the questions on his
"final" (accompanied by a drawing of himself "before" and
"after" the examination). He spent two dollars for a plaster
cast of a sculpted figure on which he sketched the nerves of
the skin (including a drawing of it in the letter along with
one of the skulls that decorated his desk).

At the opening of his second year he was buying books
right and left (he wished they were cheaper, but couldn't
resist), among them Osler's newly published *Practice of
Medicine*. He was assisting in anatomy and at "etherized"
operations, and worked in the out-patient department of
Massachusetts General Hospital. Clinical work began much
earlier in those days, and the second-year student was proudly
sporting his stethoscope. He kept a "line-a-day" diary from
which we learn that he was deeply shaken because one of
the first patients he anesthetized died on the operating table.

Talking it over with a fellow student, he decided that some method should be devised to measure the depth of anesthesia. He then developed the ether chart on which was recorded continuously the patient's pulse, respiration, and later the blood pressure, when a pneumatic device for registering it became available. From then on both surgeon and anesthetist could tell the patient's condition at a glance. The ether chart stands as one of the major American contributions to the techniques of surgery.

A quarter of a century later his former schoolmate, E. A. Codman, wrote to Cushing: "One of the things I cannot bear to dump in the wastebasket is a collection of ether charts which we made 30 years ago!"

About the middle of his third year, Cushing was faced with the need to make a decision: Should he stay on for a fourth year, or take his degree with the majority of the students in the last three-year class (1894)? The choice involved acceptance of an offer to work under Dr. Osler at Johns Hopkins, or an appointment in the out-patient department of Massachusetts General where the best upper classmen would run the department under visiting surgeons. By May he apparently had decided to stay in Boston, and that summer he went with Ned on a six-week tour of England. On his return he entered his fourth year at Harvard Medical School.

After a month or two he thanked his father for urging him to take a fourth year. "I think I am getting and am going to get much out of it. The clinics are mostly fine." In addition to his work at Massachusetts General, he spent several afternoons a week at Children's Hospital, and also carried out experimental work with an orthopedic surgeon. Among other things, this gave him an opportunity to learn a new technique in which plaster of Paris was used to fill in bony cavities in dogs.

This was also the year he began his neurological work. From his notes we learn of his interest in a patient who had been operated on for a compound fracture of the skull. He records the "fearful hemorrhage from brain sinuses," always a hazard in brain operations, the consequent fading out of the pulse, and its return with the application of pressure to stop the bleeding. He followed this patient through his discharge and convalescence. A brief assignment at the Convalescent Home in Waverley gave him additional experience with mental and neurological cases, and in the spring he received confirmation of his first appointment: house officer at Massachusetts General Hospital.

On June 16, 1895, he wrote to his mother: "Yesterday I finished my last examination in the Harvard Medical School and glad I am. If I had known what a struggle it was to be I don't believe I should ever have had the sand to begin. . . ."

He was awarded the degrees of M.D. and M.A. *cum laude*.

During his last year in Boston, Cushing was appointed to the much sought-after post of Assistant Resident in Surgery at Johns Hopkins University. The Baltimore Medical School and Hospital, organized only three years earlier, had not yet graduated its first class, but from the outset gave promise of being a top-ranking institution. Its very organization was a departure in medical education, providing for distinct units each in charge of a chief-of-service.

On its faculty were the Big Four: Sir William Osler, one of the most brilliant and influential modern teachers of medicine; William S. Halsted, leader of the advance guard of American surgeons; William Henry Welch, pathologist and medical historian; and Howard Atwood Kelly, influential Professor of Gynecology and Obstetrics and authority in American medical history. With such men it is no wonder that very early in its history Johns Hopkins had many more applicants than it could admit. Even a young man of Harvey Cushing's talents could not be sure of appointment, so when he was notified that he had been selected as Assistant Resident under Halsted, he gave up plans to study in Europe.

Ned wrote him about Halsted that "there is no surgeon like him in the land, his aseptic technique is perfect, and the scientific manner of his work, keeping at it from the laboratory side simultaneously with his clinical and operative work, is a revelation to a man."

Characteristically, Cushing took unkindly to change, and at first was far from happy with what he found in Baltimore. He thought that the hospital was a "a very sloppy place," the surgical service poorly organized, and the library inaccessible. Dr. Halsted didn't operate enough, and the rows of unbroken brick fronts in the city were "as alike as Streptococci." But before the year was out, when asked how long he expected to stay, he answered "indefinitely."

Cushing had had some experience in Boston with x-rays, which were just coming into use, and within a few weeks of his arrival at Hopkins, he was given a chance to apply the new technique. There was a patient in his emergency ward who had been shot during a family brawl, the bullet lodging in the woman's neck. From the symptoms — paralysis on one side and loss of sensation on the other — Cushing correctly located the site of the bullet and verified it with x-ray plates. This was his first case of spinal cord injury, and the next year he reported it at a meeting of the Johns Hopkins Medical

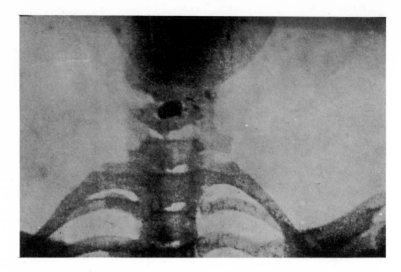

An early Johns Hopkins X-ray showing bullet in spine. From Harvey Cushing's first paper

Society and wrote it up as his first formal paper, a "maiden effort" as he told his father.

As Cushing got to know Halsted better, he came to respect him as a surgeon and teacher, but never warmed up to him as a man. We know now that this was no fault of Cushing's; he was simply unaware of Dr. Halsted's tragic story.

In 1884, when it was found that cocaine could anesthetize the eye, Halsted began to investigate its effect on the rest of the body, using himself as a guinea pig. Therefore, long before others, he discovered that cocaine was habit-forming, simply because he became addicted to it. By sheer will power he stopped using the drug, but never overcame the effects of his addiction. He became a painfully shy, unsocial person, suffering acutely at social gatherings, and outside the hospital avoided colleagues, patients, and students. His health was also affected, and he was able to operate only two or three times a week and not more than once a day. The young Cushing, impatient for operating experience, fretted over this. Only Welch, who befriended and watched over Halsted during the dreadful years of torture, knew the reason for his eccentric habits.

Halsted had studied in Austria and Germany, where aseptic surgery was far more advanced. He was among the first in America to wear the white surgical gown and skull cap, and also brought back from Europe the use of the gauze mask, introduced by Mickulicz, a noted Polish surgeon. Then he introduced rubber gloves, more for reasons of romance than asepsis. . . .

His head nurse, whom he later married, was sensitive to caustic antiseptics, and Halsted ordered rubber gloves to protect her delicate hands. When one of the surgical staff tried them and liked them, he was considered a little queer, but soon others recognized their value in aseptic surgery.

Halsted was a meticulous operator. Because he took time to tie off even the smallest vessels, his operations were almost bloodless. He handled the tissues with the utmost care and gentleness, and by insisting on exact approximation of sur-faces, avoiding all dead spaces, and using the finest suture material, he left the wounds clean and dry. His operations lasted two or three times as long as seemed necessary to others, but as a result his patients suffered a minimum of shock from the operation. He spent as much time at animal experiments in the laboratory as he did in the clinic, using his results to solve many surgical problems with rare ability, insight, and imagination.

One day early in his career at Johns Hopkins, Cushing

injected a patient with strychnine, after an operation according to "the usual procedure" he had learned in Boston.

"What do you suppose strychnine will do for the patient?"
Professor Halsted asked him.

The young surgeon was stumped, and Dr. Halsted directed him to read up on it. "If your reading convinces you
that strychnine is good for the patient, then by all means
use it."

After doing the recommended research, Cushing saw no
good reason for giving strychnine. He was deeply impressed
with the lesson: never do anything without knowing the
reason why.

At the end of his first year at Hopkins, Cushing was appointed Instructor in Surgery at a salary of $100 a year, con-
tinuing as Assistant Resident also. As he wished him well in
his new position, Dr. Welch also congratulated him on his
recovery from an appendectomy, still a risky operation in
those days. Cushing himself had made the diagnosis, and
wrote a detailed and objective case history, adding: "Operative note was left to the surgeon!" With the same objectivity
he later wrote his own convalescent history.

Late in 1897, while Halsted was away, several patients
died from ether anesthesia because of still inadequate experience with the pain killer, and Cushing began to experiment with cocaine, injecting it at the site of a nerve to produce
"block" anesthesia. His first major operation using this method
was an amputation of a cancerous arm bone at the shoulder.
Later he amputated a leg at the hip, with this local anesthetic,
and used it several times in hernia operations. In 1898 he reported this work before the Johns Hopkins Medical Society.

Harvey Cushing was always a serious and hard-working

student, but he took full advantage of all holidays and vacations, which he spent traveling, or at home in Cleveland. His "line-a-day" diary, letters to his family, and delightful pen-and-ink sketches show his keen interest in everything he saw, whether in Bermuda, Cuba, Canada, or the Chicago Exposition of 1893. And on his visits at home he missed very few of the summer festivities — dances, picnics, lawn parties, fishing.

At these affairs he was seen more often with "Kate" than any one else. Katharine Stone Crowell's family, like his own, was of pioneering stock, and she and Harvey had been friends since childhood. Attractive, witty, and high-spirited, Kate Crowell was also a steady, mature, sophisticated young woman, and her interest in Harvey must have been sorely strained if she counted on an early permanent attachment.

During his first year at Harvard, Kate visited friends in Boston and spent some time with Harvey. He saw her off and while settling her on the train he came "very near being carried to Worcester." He asked for her picture, which she sent him, and the next summer there was an "understanding" between them, but nothing like a formal engagement. They corresponded regularly and saw each other whenever he was in Cleveland.

In 1898 she came to Baltimore, staying with the Goodwillies, who were friends of both families, and the two young people were invited to the Halsteds for dinner. The Halsteds entertained so rarely that Harvey and Kate must have considered this a very special occasion. Cushing also introduced Kate to the Oslers at this time. When she returned to Cleveland, Harvey sent off a letter to "Aunt Ca'line" (Kate's mother) asking for her daughter's hand in marriage. While waiting for a reply, he wrote several frenzied letters to Kate fearing that he may have acted precipitately.

Mrs. Crowell, who was very fond of him, gave her warm consent. "There is no one to whom I could trust her as I can to you," she wrote after a few days.

That summer Kate and Harvey accompanied Ned and his wife and Harvey's mother on a Great Lakes trip to Duluth. Although everyone else now considered Kate part of the family, it was another four years before the young man finally took on the responsibilities of marriage.

In the intervening years he acted as a military surgeon in the Spanish-American war, performing many operations on typhoid perforations of the intestine, kept up with his strenuous duties as Assistant Resident, wrote papers, and studied bacteriology. He was made a member of the Hopkins Committee on Graduate Instruction, devoting much of his time to planning a program of clinical teaching. Then in 1900 he went to Europe on a year's leave of absence.

Making up his mind to take the European trip was difficult. It was another step away from becoming established in his profession, and would delay his marriage at least another year. But he told himself, and wrote to Kate, that in pursuing his goal of becoming a leading surgeon he was, after all, in great measure doing it for her.

Meeting and working with the best minds in Europe's hospitals and laboratories was just what was needed for the somewhat provincial young surgeon. In England he made the rounds of the famous London hospitals: St. George's, Guy's, University College Hospital, and the National Hospital for Paralysis and Epilepsy where Hughlings Jackson worked. He observed operations by Victor Horsley, neurosurgeon, first to remove a spinal tumor, and saw Sir Charles Sherrington conduct cortical mapping experiments in chimpanzees and orangutangs. His great interest in John Hunter began at this time. The Hunterian Museum held a special fascination, and he returned there day after day, determined to start a collection of his own. Strangely, his lifelong friendship with Osler took root here, while his teacher was on a prolonged vacation from Johns Hopkins.

Paris provided an opportunity to attend the 13th International Medical Congress in addition to strenuous " hospitalizing," sightseeing, and tasting the rich cultural life of the French capital. It was on the Pont d'Alexandre, overlooking the Seine, that Cushing, with Will Mayo, George W. Crile, and John B. Murphy (attending the Congress), hatched the idea of establishing the Society of Clinical Surgery. A group of forty younger surgeons formed this club for the purpose of exchanging ideas, not by the reading of papers, but by visiting each other's operating rooms. They looked upon most members of the American Surgical Association as "old fossils."

From Paris he went to Lyons, then to Geneva and Lausanne in Switzerland, to learn new operating techniques. "It's marvelous to see him enucleate a goitre (no anesthesia whatever, not even any morphia) in from eight to twelve minutes for the entire operation," he wrote about one surgeon.

He stayed on in Berne to work out an answer to a question posed to him by Theodor Kocher: how is the blood supply to the brain controlled in a living animal? From the time he witnessed his first brain operation in Boston, he had been impressed with the surgical problem of hemorrhage. Now, by placing a small window in the skull of an animal under anesthesia, he was able to observe by direct vision the blood vessel changes in the brain under varying conditions. This work, which he wrote up and published on his return, was an important contribution to the eventual successful control of brain hemorrhage during an operation.

In Italy he made the grand tour of Pisa, Bologna, Padua, Venice, and Pavia, taking inspiration from these landmarks, historically linked with the names of Vesalius, Fabricius, and William Harvey. From Pavia he brought back a model of an apparatus for measuring blood pressure, which he adapted for use during surgery.

In Germany he took in every medical center time would allow. Then he went back to England and to Scotland. Everywhere he was received with warm cordiality and respect for his ability and lively mind, and his hosts, charmed with his personality, showered him with hospitality. All in all, the year in Europe, with the contacts he made, the new ideas and techniques he absorbed, and the cosmopolitan outlook he developed, proved to be one of his most valuable experiences.

He returned in the fall of 1901 and spent several weeks in Cleveland making plans with Kate for their marriage the following June. Back in Baltimore, he was assigned a third-year class in Surgical Anatomy, a "practical, regional, applied &c Anatomy and which will be followed in the Spring by an *Operative* Course for which I would like to use both cadavers and animals," he wrote to his father. He was also to work in the neurological clinic, where he would have the privilege of operating on his own private patients, and was able to take over some of the work assigned to Halsted, who was frequently away, and welcomed Cushing's assistance.

With his students, Cushing was a hard taskmaster. He was impatient and irritable with anyone who showed less drive than he or failed to grasp and carry out his instructions. He would often flare up in anger, a characteristic for which his father had rebuked him even as a boy, nicknaming him "Pepper Pot." This was bound to make him enemies, so that on one occasion Osler, who was the soul of gentleness, and whose sunny disposition was legend, had to call him to task. "You will not mind a reference to one point. The statement is current that you do not get on well with your surgical subordinates & colleagues. . . . The statement also is made that you have criticized before the students the modes of dressings, operations &c of members of the staff. This, I need scarcely say, would be absolutely fatal to your success here. . . . I know you will not mind this from me as I have your interests at heart."

Cushing took this criticism as it was intended from the man he admired and wished to emulate.

While he often lost his temper, he was severely self-disciplined in his work. During operations, some of which lasted for several hours, he would not move from his assigned spot, concentrating all his attention on every minute detail, permitting no talking until the operation was over and he had made his detailed notes.

Despite the personal difficulties he had with his colleagues, his ability as a surgeon was fast gaining recognition. He was invited to give lectures, write papers, and demonstrate his blood pressure recording during anesthesia. His experimental surgery course (animal) in the newly established Hunterian Laboratory was considered so valuable that it was adopted by other schools for the training of student surgeons.

The first year after his return from Europe he shared quarters with two close friends in a house next to the Osler's. "Later on I will pretend to keep afternoon office hours 2-3, and will have a 'yaller shingle on the door,' " he wrote home. Their proximity to the cheerful Osler household made housekeeping for the three young bachelors not too onerous. In fact, the "latch-keyers," as they were dubbed because they had ready access to the house next door, had a pretty easy time of it.

After many postponements, Harvey and Kate were finally married in Cleveland in the summer of 1902, and for the next six years made their home in the "bachelor" house. One of the latch-keyers stayed on as a member of the Cushing household, while Mrs. Osler initiated Kate into the intricacies of domesticity. During the years she had waited for Harvey, Kate had learned to accommodate herself to the man whose work was his life, and now that they were married, she was even more loving and gracious. Their domestic happiness was complete when William Harvey Cushing, the first of their five children, was born in 1903. William Osler was his godfather.

By 1906, Cushing was financially comfortable and had achieved professional independence. By turning back his small stipend from the University, he was able to engage a medical student to assist him with the dog work in the Hunterian Laboratory. He also had a competent office nurse and a secretary.

The Cushings had established themselves socially in the Baltimore medical set. The Oslers left to live in England, but returned now and then for a visit at Christmas time. This year the Cushings gave them a party. Almost every Baltimore doctor and his wife attended, some came from Washington, and even the Secretary of the Navy made an appearance. Reported the *Baltimore Sun*, "Doctor and Mrs. Cushing proved themselves splendid hosts. The house was transformed into a conservatory. Banks of American Beauty roses, evergreens and palms added to the beauty of the scene, and the odor of fragrant flowers filled the house. Mrs. Osler was the center of attraction among the fair sex."

Cushing always advised his students to become good physicians first. Then if they had a special interest in neurosurgery, the brand new offshoot of surgery that was his own specialty, they should first become thoroughly competent general surgeons. He spoke from experience, because his own career began as a general surgeon and it was not until the end of 1904 that he presented his first report on "The special field of neurological surgery."

He credited Dr. Halsted with the idea of directing students toward some subdivision of surgery, and with guiding him into neurosurgery. Actually, his interest dated not from Halsted's influence but from 1895, when in Boston he had assisted at the first brain tumor operation. Even then the problems of correct diagnosis and localizing of the tumor, and the control of hemorrhage and shock, were very much on his mind, as they were later when he visited Sherrington, and when in Berne he investigated the blood supply to the brain.

Seeing Sherrington at work, he had commented at the time: "It is not impossible that a diseased pituitary body may some day be successfully attacked." As yet (1904) he had not removed a brain tumor successfully, but he favored opening the skull in "palliative trepanation" to relieve the severe pain caused by the increased pressure of an expanding tumor.

He had already achieved some success in the surgical removal of tumors compressing the spinal cord, and he had developed the technique of operating on the Gasserian ganglion, from which emerge the sensory nerves to the face, thus giving relief to patients with excruciatingly painful facial neuralgia. But during these first few years, the mortality from brain surgery was frightfully high, and many patients died without the tumor being located.

With each attempt, however, his results became more encouraging and attracted wide notice, particularly the Gasserian ganglion operation. The introduction of blood-pressure recording during operations, together with a number of new ways he devised for reducing hemorrhage, added to the safety of the procedure. He also made many improvements in the instruments used to open the skull, and developed electrodes for applying electrical stimuli to the exposed surface of the brain. In this way he was able to verify the location of a tumor according to the methods of the brain mappers and explorers.

From 1908 to 1912 he directed his primary attention to tumors of the pituitary, the gland which controls, among other things, growth and sexual development. At that time it was believed to be inaccessible to surgery, and in fact cases of pituitary tumor were almost never recognized prior to death.

In the meantime the family was growing. Mary was born in 1906, and another child was expected early in 1908. The Cushings moved to a larger house and enjoyed the added luxuries of electricity, baths, and no latch-key boarder!

A few months later he announced in a telegram to his father: "A seven and three quarters pound suffragette landed at five smooth voyage telephone Ned and others." This was the new baby, named Betsey after Harvey's mother (Mrs. Betsey Cushing died in 1903, shortly after her son's first child, William, was born).

The next year Cushing performed his first successful pituitary operation on the patient sent to him by Dr. Charles Mayo. For years the man had complained of headache, sensitivity to light, weakness, and fatigue. Then came a progressive enlargement of the tongue, lips, face, and limbs: his tongue was so large that he was unable to inhale ether, and therefore had to be given it through an opening in the windpipe. The gland was approached through an opening in the forehead, and about a third of it removed. The patient recovered and the symptoms largely subsided, although the bones of the limbs remained overgrown. Cushing kept in touch with this patient for some twenty years during which there was no recurrence of symptoms.

The same year, Cushing gave a report on his first thirty cases of cerebellar tumor, and he and Kate went to Europe, chiefly at the invitation of the International Medical Congress, held in Budapest. They did considerable sightseeing before going on to the Congress, and Cushing developed a special interest in the work of Andreas Vesalius that was to engage him for many years afterward.

By February 9, 1910, Cushing was so well known that he was called upon to examine a very famous person, and for the first time was successful in removing the type of brain tumor he found. Major General Leonard Wood, Chief of Staff of the Army, and later Governor of the Philippines, had struck his head on a low chandelier on shipboard some twelve years earlier. An intracranial tumor had formed at the site of the injury and was now pressing on the brain, producing numbness, weakness of the left side of the body, and convulsive movements of the affected limbs. Back in the Boston days, Cushing had assisted at a similar operation, and had performed the autopsy when the patient died. Nevertheless, he now advised surgery, and in a four-hour session removed a large meningeal tumor, one of the most difficult to operate on because of its rich supply of blood vessels. Eleven days later the General was able to walk about his room.

Right after the operation, an account of which appeared in all the newspapers and was read by his father, Cushing received a telegram summoning him home. His father had suffered a stroke; his right hand was paralyzed and he had temporarily lost his speech. Cushing arrived in Cleveland on February 11th. His father recognized him, saying: "I do not know what will happen, but it is all right for I have already said all that I wished to say about everything." The next day he died.

His handwritten will contained the kind of advice about money matters he always had given to his children; he bequeathed his watch to Harvey, and asked that the family property be kept together as long as possible. Of his personal belongings there was little left worth passing on; among his threadbare clothes, no suit was less than ten years old. All of Harvey's letters to him over the years, ever since the Yale days, he had preserved and neatly arranged in order.

Cushing's meteoric rise in the field of neurosurgery brought him many offers of new positions, but he repeatedly declined them until 1910, when he accepted the post of Chief Surgeon at the newly founded Peter Bent Brigham Hospital in Boston. At that time it was only a blueprint, and was not opened to patients for another two years, while Cushing impatiently fussed and fumed in Baltimore, making frequent trips to Boston to direct the new hospital's organization. These visits annoyed the Trustees so much that they voted him funds to go to Europe until the hospital was completed, but having just returned, he turned them down.

Finally in October, 1912, even with the hospital not yet ready, and the plumbers and paperhangers still camped in the family's new Boston home, Cushing was able to write:

"Everything looks promising, and the people are cordial to a degree . . . alas! . . . we are sailing into the surgical laboratory."

From Baltimore, Welch wrote that he had left a "yawning chasm," and Dean Howell added, "There is no one in sight who can begin to take your place."

As Chief Surgeon, and with the core of house officers and research men he brought with him, he was in a position of full authority; he could run things his own way — and did. His first innovation was the assignment of residents in surgery to do major procedures themselves. In this case he came to grips with, and overcame, the established policy of providing only minimum training for junior and senior interns. There were other conflicts with the administration, not all of which he was able to settle to his own satisfaction, but among his surgical team, most of them trained under him, and inspired by their chief's driving enthusiasm, there was unswerving loyalty and excellent team work.

He worked like a demon, beginning at eight in the morning and taking part of his breakfast in the office while preparing lectures, writing papers, and answering letters; then he went on his rounds. He operated several times a week, paying no attention to week ends or holidays, and after every operation wrote up his carefully detailed notes. Some of these found their way into his unique annual reports, and his biographer, John F. Fulton, comments on the one for 1913-1914: ". . . many were surprised by the detailed appendix in which every fatality which had occurred in the hospital was described in detail. The causes of death were fully indicated, even when they involved bad clinical judgment, faulty anesthesia, or a mistake in diagnosis."

Cushing firmly believed that every case, successful or not, should be scrutinized for any possible contribution to the advancement of knowledge. This is why he stressed the importance of autopsies, and it has been estimated that these were obtained in over ninety per cent of his brain tumor patients who died, before or after operation. It was not at all unusual for a staff member to be told at midnight to pack a bag and take off to almost any place on the East Coast to carry out such an examination. Even more was to be learned from his successes, which greatly outnumbered his failures.

While still at Baltimore, he had instituted a system for following up his patients, a practice he continued at Brigham. Among other things he requested his neurological patients to write him on the anniversaries of their operations. Thus he was able over the years to collect information concerning the end-results of his surgery, and to learn something about the life-expectancy of former patients with different types of tumor. At the peak of his surgical career he was following nearly a thousand such cases of brain tumor. He also inaugurated the practice of storing specimens taken from the brain tumors either at operation or autopsy, collecting over two thousand, which are still preserved as the Cushing Tumor Registry.

Just as Cushing was becoming recognized as the world's leading neurosurgeon — he had reduced the mortality rate in brain surgery from considerably more than 90 to a little over 8 per cent — his work at Brigham was interrupted by World War I. With a volunteer unit from Harvard, he went overseas for three months to care for the wounded at the American Ambulance Hospital at Neuilly. On the return voyage he was called to the forward deck. "This I did, but rather wish I had not. We were going through the *Lusitania* wreckage."

When the United States entered the war, he went over again with a unit mobilized for Base Hospital No. 5. Operating under war conditions and mainly on wounds from shell explosions, he worked for sixteen hours at a stretch with "black earth thrown up like a geyser" all around him. He devised many new operating techniques, one employing a large magnet to draw shell fragments from skull wounds. For speed and efficiency, he gave up both chloroform and ether, using local anesthesia only, as he did from then on in his own hospital.

Shortly after returning from his war service, he developed an illness involving numbness, pain, and unsteadiness in his legs. He never fully recovered and was in constant fear that it would prevent him from operating. The long hours of standing over the table did cause him considerable pain, but he continued to operate with the same delicate dexterity, never shortening his fastidious routine, and never deviating from the elaborate and painstaking techniques for which he became so well known.

As he neared the close of his active operating career, he introduced still another new technique — electrosurgery. After seeing a high-frequency current machine cut up a big block of beef, the idea struck him: why couldn't it be applied to surgery? He enlisted the help of a Harvard physicist in constructing the apparatus, and in 1926 performed an historic operation, using the current to remove a tumor, cutting the tissue with almost no bleeding. By modifying the method, he was able to coagulate blood vessels that had to be severed or were already bleeding.

"This operation was a perfect circus — many ringed," he wrote. "The New England Surgical Association was here and almost every hand was occupied with them. . . . This had necessitated re-electrifying the operation room, Dr. Gennough appeared with four or five coughing Frenchmen

Harvey Cushing in 1929 in Europe. From a photograph by Arnold C. Klebs

[visitors from France] with colds in their heads, the student who was acting as possible donor fainted and fell off the seat. . . . Then with Dr. Bovie's help I proceeded to take off most satisfactorily the remaining portion of tumor with practically none of the bleeding which was occasioned in the preceding operation . . ."

The next day he wrote to Bovie, the physicist, "In spite of the confusion of our many-ringed circus I was delighted how well the loop worked." A new era in brain surgery had been ushered in.

During the days of planning for the Peter Bent Brigham Hospital, Cushing himself set the retirement age for its surgeons at 63. In April 1931, when he had passed his 62nd birthday, the staff, without his knowledge, made elaborate

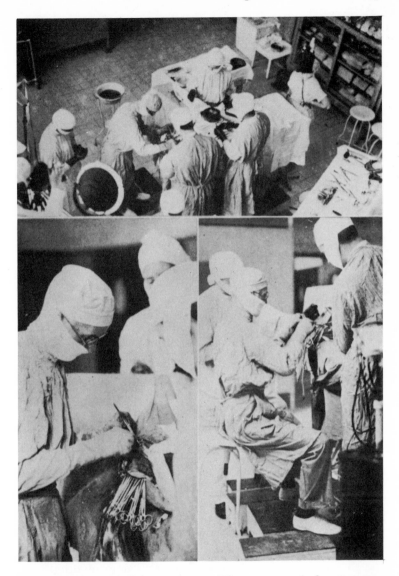

The 2,000th verified brain tumor. Three views of the operation on April 15, 1931 in which a pituitary tumor was removed. From photographs by Walter Boyd

preparations for photographs, movies, and a gala tea party for another historic occasion: Dr. Cushing performed his two-thousandth brain tumor operation! Fifteen months later, on August 17, 1932, he performed his last operation. The next day he sailed on the *Majestic* for the International Physiological Congress in Rome.

Back in Boston, he was deeply disappointed that in his absence he had been completely superseded at Brigham by his successor Dr. E. C. Cutler, and relegated to a small office previously used for photography. Because he was hurt by his altered status, during these months he characteristically entered and left the hospital by the students' entrance.

Though retired from surgery, Cushing was by no means ready to give up all activity. Several times he had been invited to join Western Reserve in Cleveland, and was offered the chair of the History of Medicine at Johns Hopkins upon Welch's retirement. He declined both.

But after a visit to New Haven, he made up his mind to accept an offer from the University to become Sterling Professor in Neurology. The circle was complete, and Cushing was happy to return to his first love, Yale. Here he continued to be active and productive, lecturing, writing, and attending meetings at home and abroad. He became a member of President Roosevelt's Medical Advisory Committee, which dealt with many complex problems, including health insurance, and participated in the work of the National Research Council. Perhaps the greatest personal satisfactions he derived from his retirement were the opportunity to devote more time to his beloved book collection on medical history, and to have a more relaxed and leisurely companionship with his family and friends.

On his seventieth birthday, the Harvey Cushing Society,

founded in 1932, held its annual meeting in New Haven. At the dinner, speeches and messages of tribute, and letters from patients, friends, and pupils, testified to the esteem in which he was held throughout the world. "You have cast new light upon the dark continent of the mind, and thereby given impetus to mortal hope and aspiration," wrote one of his grateful patients.

President Roosevelt, whose son James had married Betsey Cushing, sent a message read by the chairman: ". . . there has been no slowing down in his zest for life and for his work — a work which makes the human race his debtor and which has won him the plaudits of the great, and eternal gratitude of all sorts and conditions of men."

Among his numerous books was a biography of Osler, which won him the Pulitzer Prize, and at the time of his last, brief illness, he was working on the Bio-bibliography of Vesalius, which time did not permit him to complete. It was while lifting a heavy Vesalius folio, on the evening of October 3, 1939, that he was seized with a severe chest pain. The next day he was worse. In the hospital he was put into an oxygen tent against his strenuous objections that he couldn't look out and see what was happening. But he smiled at the news that the plans for the erection of the Medical Library at Yale, one wing of which was to house the Cushing collection, had been approved.

Three days later he died. The autopsy revealed — supreme irony — a small tumor of the brain!

His ashes were taken to Cleveland and laid to rest beside those of his parents, his brothers, and his son William who had been killed in an automobile accident years earlier.

He willed to Yale University his entire collection of books and papers.

CHAPTER FOURTEEN

Borrowed Lungs

You may have wondered more than once, while watching Westerns at the movies or on television, why gunshot or knife wounds in the chest nearly always were so quickly fatal, even when the frontier doctor was on the spot. Doctors were only too familiar with the hissing sound of air rushing in through the opening, causing the lungs to deflate. They had in fact coined a word for it — *pneumothorax,* or air-in-chest.

Because penetration of the chest wall meant almost instantaneous death, operating on the esophagus, heart, or lungs was unthinkable. Until one more surgical frontier had been crossed, it was fatal to open the chest: the lungs collapsed and breathing stopped.

Strange as it seems, the first surgeon who deliberately *created* pneumothorax did it to *prevent* pneumothorax of a diseased lung. In tubercular patients, the lung often was damaged by the rupture of a tubercle, a nodule formed by the tuberculosis germ. When the tubercle ruptured, air from the lungs escaped into the chest cavity and eventually caused the lung to collapse, just as if air had been sucked in through a stab wound. One daring surgeon had an idea of how to circumvent this — John B. Murphy, born in 1857.

———

Michael Murphy and Ann Grimes were among the many who came to the Land of Promise in the 1840s to escape the potato blight and famine in Ireland. Their paths merged during their families' search for land in the West, and they married and settled down on a farm in Appleton, Wisconsin. Soon they could write with pride to their relatives that they owned land and had a meal of meat and potatoes every day. But with all their land and fine crops, there was very little cash, and they brought up their five children to appreciate the value of money almost as much as the value of honesty and decency.

Denied the opportunity for themselves, they instilled in their children the importance of a good education. John, their youngest, well remembered his mother's credo: "If you are educated, there are no man's achievements which you cannot equal or excel, provided you have industry and integrity and are temperate."

John was imaginative, inventive, and independent, and his mother was determined that he would some day have a better life. The boy grew up hating poverty and vowing to get away from the dull routine and stern self-denial his parents were forced to accept.

In Appleton's high school, he was a credit to Mr. Schmidt, his teacher and first hero, who taught him some practical chemistry and introduced him to the art of "debating." John also had a part-time job in the town drug store. He earned fifty cents a week and saved nearly all of it for his later education.

One day Dr. Reilly, who had his office over the drug store, rushed in while John was carefully rolling pills.

"Could you give me a hand? I have a boy with a mangled leg. His brother brought him in, but he's in a dead faint."

John hurried upstairs after the doctor, who already had lifted the unconscious boy onto a bed. "Sure you can stand the sight of a little blood, or will I have to stretch you out too?" the doctor asked, throwing a quick glance in John's direction.

"Naw, I'll be all right," John assured him.

The doctor was putting a tourniquet on the injured youth's leg. "Now when I tell you, turn the stick in the knot just so much; when I tell you to loosen, turn it the other way."

John watched the doctor and did as he was told. Taking the threaded needles from his lapel, Dr. Reilly did the necessary suturing and told him seriously, "Much obliged. You did fine, my boy."

Some months later when Dr. Reilly was returning from a call, he stopped his buggy long enough to say to John: "Sure could have used you this morning."

By this time John had made up his mind to become a doctor, although Mr. Schmidt was urging him to go into teaching. As soon as he finished high school he became Dr. Reilly's apprentice, but still had to continue working in the drug store to help out with the family's expenses. By saving his pennies he managed to buy a Gray's *Anatomy*, which he studied every night into the wee hours of the morning.

After four years of apprenticeship, Dr. Reilly had taught the young man all that he could, and told Mrs. Murphy, "He's a born doctor."

In 1878 John was twenty-one and, with the help of Dr. Reilly, entered Rush Medical College in Chicago for his formal medical education. Mrs. Murphy dipped into the savings she kept in a teapot, part of which came from bounty money her boys earned by shooting wolves. This would take care of the first year's tuition of sixty-five dollars.

"See that you're a credit to your mother," were Mr. Murphy's parting words to his son.

Dr. Reilly's choice of a medical school was a wise one. There were many brilliant teachers at Rush, among them Christian Fenger, a master in diagnosis who was well schooled in the latest surgical methods used in the German clinics. Fenger took a liking to the young man and saw great promise in him, and when Murphy graduated, the doctor helped him to obtain an internship in Cook County Hospital. He also introduced him to Dr. Edward W. Lee, who needed an assistant.

Murphy was restless during his first few months with Dr. Lee, less interested in his practice than in continuing his education in Europe in the clinics Fenger had told him about. It was not an impossible dream, for in those days it didn't take so much money for the crossing. He had a little of his own, and Mrs. Murphy once again gambled her hard-earned savings on the confidence she had placed in her son. Dr. Lee offered to help with the rest, and further encouraged his assistant with the parting words: "Your name will be on the door when you come back."

So in 1882 Murphy went to Vienna to study under Theodor Billroth, who had pioneered in stomach surgery. Billroth warmly welcomed him as a student of Fenger's, whom he had himself tutored in surgery, and Murphy showed his appreciation with a thirst for knowledge that was unquenchable.

He worked seven days a week, taking off only the few hours
he needed for sleep, and let the pleasures of the gay city on
the Danube go by. For lack of funds he often went hungry,
and whether from overwork, lack of food, or both, he developed what Billroth diagnosed as tuberculosis of the kidneys. He advised the young student to return home and regain
his health.

But Murphy simply could not face the prospect of giving
up his studies and perhaps even his career as a surgeon. Instead, he decided to go to Berlin, where perhaps he would
get a different diagnosis, and signed up to work in a Berlin
clinic. For whatever reason, his health improved, and the
next year he went on to Heidelberg, conscientiously making
the round of all the hospitals in which Fenger had worked.
Then early in 1884 Dr. Lee asked him to return: the older
man had more patients than he could handle.

Realizing his obligations, Murphy reluctantly came back,
but having hobnobbed with Europe's best surgeons, he was
far from satisfied with the life of a neophyte general practitioner. What chance was there for him to become a well-
known surgeon if he had to spend all his time making routine
calls to poor foreign-born families in Chicago's slums?

His ambition was soon rewarded by Dr. Nicholas Senn,
one of his former teachers at Rush Medical, who secured an
appointment for him as Instructor of Surgery at the college,
and by Dr. Lee himself, who got him into Cook County
Hospital as a full-fledged attending surgeon. In both positions
his European training proved to be an asset; during these
years American surgery was just beginning. And if he
couldn't have wealthy patients, at least he had an opportunity
to do surgery in the hospital.

One evening a call came in from Chicago's then fashionable West Side. Dr. Lee was engaged and sent Murphy to take the call. The visit was to mark a turning point in the young surgeon's life, for his patient was the charming young daughter of Alfred Plamondon, one of Chicago's wealthiest manufacturers of machinery parts.

Murphy made an immediate impression on the eighteen-year-old girl, and her parents showed their approval by telling him he could come again the next day instead of Dr. Lee. The illness turned out to require many visits and a full-blown romance developed. Nettie was deeply in love with John; she was also sure that he was a genius, and secretly planned to guide him along the road to success as a surgeon. At their wedding, Ann Grimes Murphy stood proudly at the altar. Her fondest dreams had come true: her son would enjoy both wealth and education.

Nettie wasted no time in getting her campaign into operation. In the fine home her parents had given the young couple as a wedding gift she set up a research laboratory; John now had his own office at a good address, and Nettie became his devoted assistant. Now indeed his European training was to pay rich dividends.

Dr. Murphy was rapidly developing a reputation for brilliant and daring surgery. His mechanical skill was of the highest order, his aseptic techniques almost second nature, and he immediately attracted attention by his operations for appendicitis. In this procedure he blazed the trail in America and thrust himself into the center of a hot controversy. He would operate at the first signs of inflammation, on the kitchen table or on the sofa in the patient's home if hospital space was not available immediately, and in four years had collected more than 250 cases. The older surgeons raised their hands in horror. Murphy was accused of "operating on

John Benjamin Murphy, M.D. (1857–1916)

everything and padding his figures" (of successful operations).

His dramatic successes and forceful personality caught the popular fancy and his name appeared more and more often in the newspapers. Tall, powerfully built, with a florid complexion and carefully parted red beard, he cut a striking figure. His rough-and-ready manner, quick movements, decisive speech, infectious enthusiasm, and genuine feeling for his patients set him apart from his stuffy colleagues. Reporters found him an appealing subject, but every story was another red flag to the conservative Chicago doctors. It was rumored that this whippersnapper was too greedy for quick recognition, nothing but a publicity seeker. The older men grumbled and the envious incompetents hated him.

By 1890 Murphy had two assistants who had been his students both at Rush and at the hospital, so that it was said they were "copies of him." Together they carried on experiments in his private laboratory, so conveniently arranged by Nettie. Even though there were now two children, she saw as her first duty the furtherance of her husband's career, helped him in the laboratory and in the preparation of speeches and papers, and made sure he made the right professional connections.

In the midst of this feverish grind his old tubercular infection became active, this time in his lungs. A friend persuaded him to go to New Mexico for the reputed curative effects of the desert climate, but as soon as he thought the disease had been arrested, he was back in Chicago.

Within three months he had invented a device that was to revolutionize abdominal surgery. One day he came storming into the house, swept his young wife off her feet, and whirled her around the room.

"Nettie, I've got it!" he shouted gleefully. Folding back the hem of her skirt, he showed her how the little gadget worked — just like a dressmaker's snap fastener! We still know it as the *Murphy button*, used to join the ends of a divided intestine. Instead of endless hours of suturing, with the patient likely to die from shock, the little button that looked like a sleigh-bell could be snapped into place in a few seconds. This made possible many life-saving operations on the stomach, intestines, and gall bladder.

The Murphy button soon found its way into the operating rooms of the larger hospitals, the Mayos being among the first to use it. The American doctor was invited to address the International Medical Congress in Rome and was made an honorary member of the German Surgical Society. But in Chicago his invention only further aroused the enmity of his colleagues, the most vitriolic attack coming from his old teacher, Nicholas Senn, who was now a rival. Dr. Murphy was accused of having copied the "invention" from a French investigator, and once again was charged with the unethical act of announcing his work in the press. Murphy fought back, less with words than with more innovations.

***

The Murphys by this time had moved to a large mansion on fashionable Michigan Avenue, and Mrs. Murphy had seen to it that here too the doctor had a laboratory.

It was perhaps natural that he should turn to a possible cure for tuberculosis. His two brothers and a sister had died from consumption, and he himself had not completely recovered from the ravaging disease. The idea of pneumothorax came to him after performing an autopsy on a child whose lung condition had improved after many months under his care, but who had died in a traffic accident. He found that several of the tubercular cavities had healed, precisely where the sickly discharge accumulating in the chest cavity had compressed the lung. He concluded that the signs of recovery in the girl must have been due to the enforced rest the lung received during its slow, partial collapse.

Why not induce pneumothorax artificially, the daring doctor asked himself. If the lung were spared the constant stretching with each breath, perhaps the damaged tissue would heal. The problem then became one of producing a state of complete rest by applying moderate pressure on the lungs without making a hole in the chest.

Murphy and his assistants performed numerous experiments on animals to see whether it was possible to introduce air slowly into the pleural cavity without causing *sudden* collapse of the lung.

First Murphy tried to find a substance which, when introduced slowly into the chest, would simulate the compression caused by the discharge from the diseased lung; such a substance must not be readily absorbed, or the pressure on the lung would not be sustained. Oily fluids compressed the lung too much; air introduced through a needle was effective but was soon absorbed. Finally, he found that nitrogen met both of these objections, and it was time to try the method on humans.

Apparatus for injecting nitrogen into the chest cavity

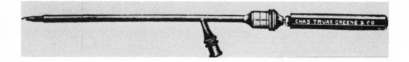

Tube with pinpoint opening

Murphy's procedure consisted of making a tiny incision in the skin between two ribs under a local anesthetic. Then he introduced a narrow tube with a sharp pin-point opening through which nitrogen was slowly forced into the cavity. This condition of artificial pneumothorax could be so regulated that just enough nitrogen was introduced to compress the affected lung without interfering with the work of the other lung or the heart.

Murphy found that the patients suffered no distress from the operation, and could be discharged from the hospital almost immediately. After several months the immobilized and rested lung healed. The cough disappeared, the fever and night sweats were reduced, the patients regained their appetite and gained weight.

Murphy announced his new treatment for tuberculosis at a meeting of the American Medical Association held in Denver in 1898. His paper, *Surgery of the Lung*, by its very name created a sensation in the medical world. The doctors at first were incredulous, but the method was to be used for decades afterwards to save the lives of many tubercular patients.

Dr. Murphy went on to other successes in surgery on nerves, bones, and joints, and came to be known as a master surgeon and an eloquent and inspiring teacher. William Mayo spoke of him as "the surgical genius of our generation" and "without a peer" as a teacher of clinical surgery. Just before his death in 1916, he was honored by the Pope with the title of Knight-Commander of the order of Saint Gregory the Great.

Murphy's pioneering operation was but the beginning of lung surgery. There remained the unsolved problem of how to work inside the open chest, how to tackle an obstructed esophagus, for example, without death from lung collapse.

Why do the lungs promptly deflate when the chest is penetrated?

At birth, the lungs are the same size as the rib cage. As the child grows, its chest or thorax grows somewhat more than the lung cavity. As a result, on breathing *in*, when the chest expands, the lungs tend to pull away from the chest wall. This elastic recoil of the stretched lungs leaves a narrow space between the lungs and thoracic wall, creating a partial vacuum. The pressure inside the lungs, which is the same as that of the atmosphere, is therefore normally always greater than the pressure in the thorax. If the thoracic wall is pierced, air rushes in through the opening, the pressure on the lungs is increased, and they collapse.

The doctor who undertook to solve the problem of open chest surgery was steered onto this research by the Polish surgeon, Johannes von Mikulicz. The surgeon saw patients wasting way from starvation because blockage of the lower part of the gullet prevented swallowing. Operation on the esophagus could save their lives, if one could get to this organ safely.

Ferdinand Sauerbruch was a young resident assistant in surgery at a small German hospital. He was just two years out of medical school, and had already decided that the life of a country doctor was stifling. So he had taken the assistantship in the hospital at Erfurt, Germany. Although he had not distinguished himself particularly as a student, when he began to work in surgery he suddenly realized that his interest was in research.

As happens to many a young man who does not find himself until after he has completed his schooling, Sauerbruch now knew what he really wanted to do: experimentation in surgery. Since the small hospital at Erfurt offered no opportunity for that sort of career, he moved on to Berlin-Moabit Hospital. Here he was assistant to Professor Langerhans, discoverer of the cluster of cells in the pancreas now known to produce insulin. Sauerbruch's first paper, dealing with intestinal injuries, attracted the attention of the celebrated stomach surgeon and teacher at the University of Breslau, Johannes von Mikulicz. Recognizing the young man's scientific turn of mind, he invited him to Breslau as a volunteer assistant. That was in 1903.

For a long time Mikulicz had been concerned with the problem of cancer of the esophagus. If only there were a way of operating, precious years could be added to the patient's life. But thoracic surgery was a field where investigative work had to start from scratch. Would Sauerbruch undertake to study it? The younger man at once realized the potentialities of the proposed work: here was a field in which to make a name for himself.

His master arranged for him to work at the nearby Pharmacological Institute, where there were laboratory facilities and he could have all the dogs and rabbits he wanted. He would, however, still have to carry on his regular surgical duties at the hospital. Sauerbruch eagerly accepted the challenge.

First he tried operating with the animals under artificial

respiration, pumping air into the exposed lungs through an opening in the trachea (windpipe). But the amount of air forced into the lungs couldn't be controlled: the lungs swelled and the circulation was blocked. He then tried opening one side of the chest. This time the blood accumulated in the collapsed lung, and the animal struggled to get enough oxygen from the other lung, which, though inflated, was pushed to one side. After a few labored breaths and suffocating movements, the animal expired.

And it was then that a completely new idea came to Dr. Sauerbruch. Since the pressure in the thorax is slightly lower than atmospheric pressure, if the operation could be performed under this lower pressure, the lungs would not collapse. So he constructed a cylindrical glass box in the shape of a drum to fit over the dog's chest. The ends of the cylinder were covered with heavy paper. The dog's head protruded through an opening on one side, and its legs through a hole in the other. He cut two additional holes on the head side of the drum for the operator's hands. Then he made a small opening for a rubber tube, attached to a gauge, through which the required pressure could be maintained. The edges of all the openings were then taped up to make them air tight.

Now this low-pressure chamber was ready for use. Sauerbruch made a few large incisions in the dog's chest, and watched through the glass. The dog continued to breathe, the lungs did not collapse and remained their normal pink color. The experiment worked!

But it was a makeshift apparatus, and just as the elated scientist became lost in his vision of how it could be adapted for humans, something went wrong. The position he had to assume, with his hand sealed into the openings, was very awkward. Somehow his arm must have moved, tearing the paper and breaking the seal. The air was sucked into the cylinder with a hissing sound, the dog gasped a few times, and was dead before the seal could be repaired.

But it was clear that pneumothorax could be avoided under lower than atmospheric pressure. The box required only technical improvements — rubber instead of paper — to prevent such accidents.

He continued his experiments, opening the chests of many dogs, and sewing up the incisions under low pressure. The animals survived the operation and when their wounds healed they behaved normally.

The next step was to construct a chamber large enough to accommodate the surgeon and one assistant; for the present it was to be used only for operating on animals. The roof of this sub-pressure cabinet was made of glass, so that the operation could be observed from the outside. Communication between the operators and workers outside was by sign language, since the voice could not be heard above the noise of the vacuum pump that regulated the air pressure.

The low-pressure cabinet was hardly the most comfortable place for the operators; the air became hot and humid, and the operators emerged from it wilted and soaking wet. But it could be done, since the low pressure itself caused no discomfort.

When Sauerbruch had finally convinced his skeptical teacher that the low-pressure cabinet worked, the two carried on operations on the thorax of the dog, and Mikulicz performed one in which he removed part of the esophagus.

When the cabinet was ready to be demonstrated to an audience of foreign visitors, someone suggested an idea that reversed the low-pressure method. Could not the same thing be accomplished by *increasing* the pressure in the lungs? This also should prevent the collapse of the lungs while eliminating the discomfort of confinement in the low-pressure chamber? By this method the dog's head remained in the cabinet, breathing air under higher than atmospheric pressure, while the operators were working outside the cabinet. This brought about another technical problem. The anesthetist who was closeted in the chamber with the head of the dog was subjected to the chloroform fumes, and had to leave the cabinet at intervals to prevent his being overcome.

There was no pneumothorax with either of the two methods, but the inventor of the low-pressure cabinet persisted in his efforts to develop this system for operating on human beings. He believed that the high-pressure method was "not natural," interfered with the circulation, and would further tax the already overburdened heart of a patient under anesthesia. Sauerbruch abandoned the idea of the high-pressure method, and was preparing to demonstrate his cabinet before the German Society of Surgery at its June meeting in 1904.

While Sauerbruch was making elaborate preparations for the meeting, Professor Ludolph Brauer of Heidelberg was working on a simplification of the entire procedure which made the cumbersome and expensive cabinet, with all its drawbacks, unnecessary.

Brauer's plan was to construct an airtight mask, that could be fitted over the face and connected with an oxygen container under the desired hyperpressure. The oxygen also would pass through a bottle of ether, so that both the anesthetic and oxygen could be given under higher than atmospheric pressure. This system proved workable in actual operations on animals.

Nevertheless, the Breslau group continued to work with

their low-pressure cabinet. The first trial with a human failed, for a never-explained reason: despite all the precautions of reserve pumps and safety devices, something went wrong and the patient died from pneumothorax. After the two surgeons had recovered from the shock of the accident, they successfully removed a tumor under the sternum (breast bone) and performed several other successful operations. And once, during an operation for breast cancer, when the chest was accidentally pierced, Sauerbruch rushed the patient into the low-pressure cabinet and saved her life.

Eventually, although its inventor was credited with the first operation on the open chest, the Sauerbruch cabinet was abandoned. Brauer's far simpler hyperpressure method is essentially the one in use today, but further improvements were to come, employing the principle of "borrowing" both heart and lungs.

Open chest surgery was the first necessary step toward surgery on the open heart. Today the surgeon is able to empty the heart completely of blood, even stop its beating, then operate unhurriedly under direct vision, unhampered by hemorrhage or the pulsation of the cardiac muscle. The ingenious device that has made possible the correction of defects inside the heart itself is the heart-lung machine.

Since the work on a mechanical substitute for the heart and lungs began, less than three decades ago, many different people and laboratories have contributed to its development. Team work replaced the isolated effort of a single scientist, and several types of machines were constructed, each an improvement on the others.

One of these, engineered by John H. Gibbon, Jr. of

Philadelphia, oxygenates the blood by having it pass in a thin film over stainless steel screens in an atmosphere of oxygen. Using this machine, which Dr. Gibbon calls "The Queen Mary," he succeeded, in 1953, in repairing a large defect in the wall between the right and left sides of the heart of an eighteen-year-old girl. In 1960, Dr. Gibbon was one of four American physicians chosen for the Annual Gairdner Foundation International Awards, started in Canada.

Another type of machine was developed in 1955 under the direction of C. Walton Lillehei of the University of Minnesota: the helix-reservoir heart-lung machine. It is said to be the fulfillment of a wish expressed one day by Dr. Herbert E. Warden in the Minnesota laboratory: "If only a patient could be plugged into an oxygen supply the way a fetus is plugged into its mother."

Today this remarkable invention is wheeled into the operating room for open-heart surgery. The most conspicuous part of the machine is a huge cylindrical reservoir containing a coil of pipe; this is connected with a pump, heater, debubbler, oxygen tank, mixing chamber, and a tangle of tubes.

The surgical team makes ready to "plug" the machine into the patient. It is set to deliver five liters of blood each minute — more than enough for safe open-heart surgery. The chest is opened and the machine connected with the patient's venous circulation through tubes inserted into the two main veins that normally return the blood to the right side of the heart. Instead of being pumped by the heart, the blood now runs by gravity into an oxygenator set about two feet below the level of the heart.

Through another tube, oxygen also enters the oxygenator, passing through a series of holes to form large bubbles that mix with the blood. The blood takes up the oxygen and releases carbon dioxide just as it does in the lung. The excess gas rises to the top of the oxygenator, where it is connected with the debubbler, from which the bubbles escape through

Heart-lung machine (showing the coil of pipe in the cylindrical reservoir) which maintains the circulation of the blood while by-passing the heart during open-heart surgery

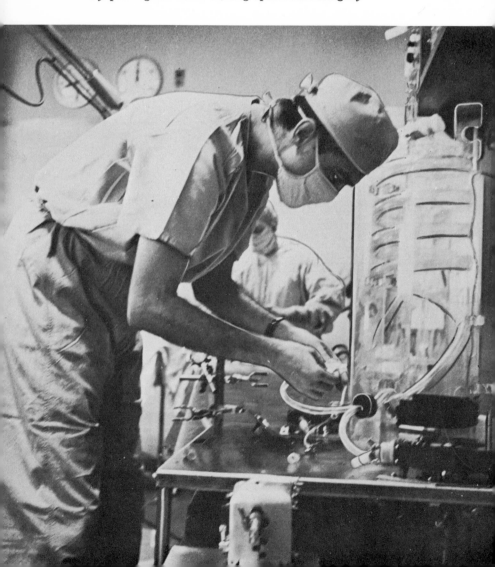

a screened vent. This is necessary to prevent free gas bubbles from entering and blocking the patient's blood vessels.

The blood then passes by gravity from the debubbler to the helix reservoir with its coil (helix) of plastic tubing. Enough turns are provided in the coil to hold a one-minute supply of oxygenated blood. The coil is surrounded by a water bath with a temperature thermostatically controlled at that of the body. From the helix-reservoir the blood is pumped toward the patient. The reservoir and the pump simulate the normal beating heart.

Via another tube the pump delivers blood to the large artery in the thigh. Thus the heart-lung machine flushes the entire circulatory system and returns the blood to the venous circulation. The circle is completed when the blood flows out once more from the two large veins to the oxygenator.

The heart muscle itself receives oxygenated blood through its own branches of the arterial system, the coronary arteries, and continues beating although its chambers are empty. By means of this recirculating system, the heart receives its normal nutrition; this permits prolonged operations for the correction of complicated defects.

Should it be necessary to stop the heart beat for the duration of an operation, a portion of the blood from the helix-reservoir is shunted through a smaller reservoir, pumped into a smaller coil which is immersed in an ice bath, and thus chilled before being "piped" into the blood vessels of the heart muscle.

A modification of this device has recently been used by a team at Toronto General Hospital. Saline ice chips, placed directly on the heart, reduced the temperature of the organ to 4° C. for forty minutes, while a repair job was done on the aorta of a fifteen-year-old patient with rheumatic fever. "We were desperate for a safer means of correcting the aortic valves without coronary cannulae [tubes] in place to feed the heart muscle with blood," explained Dr. Raymond O. Heimbecker, head of the surgical team.

The operation over, the aortic clamp is released and the warm blood starts to recirculate. Within a few minutes the heart is rewarmed and its beat restored. The patient is "unplugged" and the heart-lung machine removed in steps, reversing those which set it into operation.

Since all the parts of the machine in contact with the blood are made of plastic, they are removed and discarded. The stainless steel connectors are easily cleaned and sterilized for use in the next patient.

The "borrowed lung" has solved the problem of the open chest, so that operations can be done safely on the lungs, the esophagus, and the open heart, and for the removal of tumors in the chest. A plastic patch may be sewed into a hole in the wall of the heart, an artificial "pacemaker" installed, damage to the valves resulting from crippling diseases repaired, constriction of the aorta released, leaks between the heart chambers mended.

And these are only beginnings . . .

CHAPTER FIFTEEN

Not a Drop to Spill

In every operation — whether it be the removal of tonsils or a brain tumor — even today the surgeon must reckon with the problem of hemorrhage. Think what it was like in the past!

For centuries surgery of the thyroid, for example, was taboo. The great risk was fatal hemorrhage: for its size, this little gland receives many times more blood than any other organ in the body. Until the 1880s when Theodor Kocher in Switzerland — the only surgeon ever to receive the Nobel Prize (1909) — found a way to tie off all its blood vessels, to attempt this operation would have been considered criminal butchery.

Knowledge of the nature of the blood, what it does, and how it flows in its closed vessels developed gradually, and as it did, ways were found not only to check its escape but to replace excessive loss. Today it is rare for a patient to die from hemorrhage, but less than a hundred years ago, even when it was controlled during surgery, there was still the danger of postoperative bleeding. It was so common that in many hospitals surgical interns were assigned to the night wards along with the nurses to watch for the first signs of hemorrhaging.

Ambroise Paré spent most of his life battling to establish the use of the ligature instead of the brutal and damaging hot-iron cautery after amputation, and the ligature was an important surgical advance. But not all those who contributed to the control of hemorrhage were surgeons. Even the meaning behind the usefulness of the ligature did not become clear until 1628, when William Harvey, the "Father of Physiology," discovered that blood *circulates*. The surgeon now knew that to prevent the blood's gushing from an *artery*, he had to tie the vessel *above* where it was cut or toward the heart; to prevent its trickling from a *vein*, he had to ligature it *below* the cut or *away from* the heart.

When anesthetics made unnecessary the speedy, slap-dash surgery of the eighteenth century, it became possible to give increasing care to the checking of bleeding at every step of the operation.

When technicians devised the hemostat, a scissor-shaped instrument with overlapping saw-toothed edges, every bleeding point could be clamped off by pinching the blood vessels, even if there were a dozen or more and the hemostats ringed the incision.

Then the problem of wound infection was solved, aseptic surgery became routine, and surgeons turned their attention to the attainment of the "bloodless field." The undisputed pioneer in making operations nearly bloodless was William Halsted. What if the operation lasted four or five hours! His patience was inexhaustible when it came to stopping up every tiny bleeding vessel. Meticulous care and gentle handling of the tissues became the watchwords in this new type of surgery.

Harvey Cushing, Halsted's eminent pupil, was just as fastidious as his teacher. In addition, he was inventive. Even as a student he was deeply impressed by the magnitude of the problem of bleeding in brain surgery and studied ways of overcoming it. At first he used a broad elastic bandage around the skull to cut down surface bleeding. The freely bleeding skull bones he plugged with bone wax. For hemorrhaging tumors he invented the "Cushing clip."

Long before people knew how blood clotted, surgeons must have noticed that repeated sponging not only made the surgical field visible but somehow brought about a clotting that *stopped* the oozing and seeping. As the process came to be understood, the chemists got to work to separate the elements in blood responsible for its clotting. About two decades ago a Harvard team found a way to fractionate blood plasma, the fluid part of the blood. One "fraction" was fibrinogen, the plasma protein from which the threads form that give cohesion to the blood clot. Another was thrombin, the enzyme in plasma which changes the fibrinogen into fibrin, the insoluble substance of the tough, elastic clot threads.

The fractions, and a combination of the two — fibrinogen-thrombin — were made into a number of blood-clotting, life-saving, surgical aids. These became especially useful in the very places where hemostats, bandages, tourniquets, and other pressure-inducing devices could not be used. You can put a tight bandage on a finger to control bleeding, but not on an internal organ.

Fibrin was prepared in the form of strong, clear, plastic-like sheets of film. The brain surgeon places a piece of this film on the exposed brain to induce clotting and check bleeding. Thrombin alone, made into a powder and a solution, can be sprinkled directly on wounds or sprayed on bandages to help clotting. Another form of these natural chemicals is a light foam, and still another a sponge that can be *left in the wound* after it has done the job of stopping the bleeding! Being made of natural blood substances it is "digested," and in time disappears in the tissues. Today these artificial yet natural blood-clotters, like disinfectants and anesthetics, are routine supplies in the operating room.

As the techniques improved, surgeons became better trained, suture materials were perfected, and new blood-clotting aids were introduced, surgical and postoperative hemorrhage became less and less of a risk.

Side by side with these developments came measures for replacing lost blood. The idea of transfusing blood is at least three centuries old, but *safe* transfusion did not become a reality until about twenty-five years ago. Today we can understand the bewilderment and frustration of the early doctors who saw their patients suddenly die as they were being infused with blood that should have saved their lives.

The first transfusion, in 1665, was made from dog to dog. Richard Lower, an Englishman, having seen beer and wine successfully injected into the circulation, thought that blood would be more suitable. The dog on which he tried it was none the worse for the transfusion: it rolled on the grass, lapped the wound, and soon began to lick its master's hand.

Shortly afterwards, Jean Baptiste Denis, physician to King Louis XIV, transfused blood from a young, healthy dog into a sick, mangy cur, and both lived. He began to think: why not save people the same way? Like most pioneers, he found the going rough. It wasn't easy to convince older doctors, in the habit of *bleeding* their patients, that transfusion would make them better, and they regarded this new-fangled idea with suspicion and hostility. Transfusions had to be given pri-

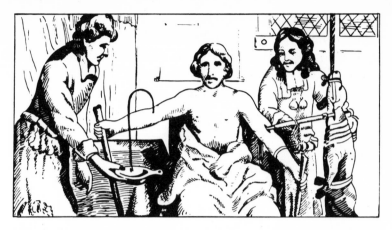

Blood transfusion from animal to man as practiced late in the seventeenth century

vately, unofficially, and at the doctor's and the patient's risk.

Denis's first transfusion patient was a sixteen-year-old boy who had suffered for months with a weakening fever. Several bleedings had only made him worse: he became dull, lost his memory, fell asleep at meals. Denis gave him a transfusion of blood from a lamb, and the boy became gay and cheerful, ate and slept well. A second patient similarly improved, but the third died.

He was a madman brought by his wife to Dr. Denis. The first two transfusions seemed to make him better, so she brought him for a third, which proved to be fatal. Denis had plenty of enemies among his colleagues, and three of them urged the widow to bring the doctor to trial. The court acquitted him of the murder charge, but decreed that from then on transfusions were to be given only with the permission of the Paris Faculty of Physicians.

As we know now, other accidents had to follow and did. As a result, in 1678 a law was passed in France, and similar

James Blundell

ones in other countries, prohibiting transfusions entirely. This world-wide prohibition lasted for 150 years.

Then in 1829, in England, James Blundell revived the practice, giving blood to mothers after childbirth. Using human donors, he transfused the blood directly from the artery into the patient's vein. He also invented a syringe and funnel with a pump that helped to force the blood into the patient. Blundell was lucky: knowing nothing about blood typing, he saved eleven of his fifteen patients. Other physicians added refinements to the technique, one of them a fine sieve to screen out the clots.

But transfusions were bound to be unsafe until the major cause of the many accidents was discovered. This was not until 1901, when Dr. Karl Landsteiner, a Viennese, found that all blood was not the same: there were four types in humans. If the donor's blood and that of the recipient were incompatible, the red cells formed clumps and the patient died. Landsteiner's discovery was the needed breakthrough.

The first doctor to use blood typing in transfusion was George W. Crile, Cleveland surgeon and close friend of Cushing. For several years Crile had devoted himself to studying surgical shock, which more frequently than anything else turned an otherwise successful operation into a fatality.

Shock was nothing new, but most surgeons regarded it as inevitable, just as a century earlier doctors had accepted pain and infection as unavoidable. The symptoms were all too familiar: ashen pallor, clammy skin, lips and fingertips blue from oxygen hunger; a vacant stare in the deeply sunken eyes; limbs cold, limp, and motionless; the hardly perceptible pulse so feeble and the blood pressure so low that one would have thought the blood vessels were nearly empty — as indeed they were.

No one knew why patients went into shock, or what could be done to restore them to normal. Since they always were cold, doctors tried to keep them warm by piling on blankets and giving them warm drinks and stimulants if they were conscious and could swallow. But recoveries were rare.

Crile focused his attention on the blood pressure drop. He put dogs into shock and injected the newly isolated adrenalin to raise their blood pressure. Adrenalin worked—even restoring the beat of a stopped heart — but only for a while. He next attempted to prevent shock by putting the dog into a rubber suit he devised. The suit was pneumatic; that is, it could be inflated with air, and when the pressure on the body was high enough, it reduced the fall in blood pressure. This too proved to be only a temporary measure: the rise in blood pressure was slight and fleeting. Then he tried transfusion and found that it not only raised the dog's blood pressure but *kept* it at the normal level. Perhaps this was the answer.

In 1905, Crile utilized Landsteiner's discovery of blood types in doing his first transfusion in a human patient by the direct method of Blundell. Donor and patient lay side by side on two operating tables, the artery of one connected with the other's vein. But Crile had some difficult moments during this life-saving procedure.

How much blood was flowing from the donor? There was no way of telling. Of course if the donor was cheerful and talkative, and his complexion was normal, all was going well. But if he turned cold, was gasping for breath, and the color left his cheeks, he was "bled too low." And if he lost too much blood, the patient must have been receiving too much — more than his overloaded heart could pump. There was also the danger of blood clots forming in the tube and stopping up the patient's blood vessels.

During the next decade transfusions were rarely used. Then, in 1914, came the next breakthrough, this time from Argentina, where Luis Agote made the important discovery that sodium citrate would prevent clotting. Now the pint of blood could be collected in a bottle containing a few crystals of the anti-coagulating chemical, and the donor could go home while the blood was slowly flowing from the bottle into the patient's vein. What had been a major operation had become a simple procedure, and a safer one. Still many technical problems remained.

When a patient needs a transfusion there is seldom any time to waste. And if time is saved by determining the patient's blood type before the operation, it may not be easy to find a suitable donor, because even members of the same family often have different types of blood.

Dr. Crile continued to study the causes of shock and to perform transfusions whenever feasible, but the many risks

George Washington Crile (1864–1943)

and difficulties prevented others from adopting the procedure. Blood typing was seldom done; in fact, the importance of Landsteiner's great contribution went largely unrecognized until 1930, when he received the Nobel Prize for the work he had done nearly thirty years earlier.

Meanwhile, in World War I, thousands of soldiers were dying, not as many from wounds as from their aftermath — shock. The symptoms were the same as those from long-drawn-out operations. Loss of blood was not always the cause, because some, who had bled only slightly, died from shock. And on the battlefield the surgeons were more helpless than they were back home in their operating rooms.

Even if they were ready to try transfusions, few knew the technique of blood typing and fresh blood was not handy, certainly not in the vast amounts needed, for nearly every wounded man was a victim of shock. So many died who could have been saved had the doctors only known what shock was and how to treat it.

But from the tragic holocaust one clue emerged. The doctors noticed one thing in all cases of fatal shock: the blood had become dark and thick — almost black, and too thick to flow. They could explain the first: fresh blood owes its bright red color to the oxygen it carries; and when deprived of oxygen it becomes purplish blue. But why the thickening that turned the flow into a sluggish crawl? Somehow, somewhere, the blood had lost part of its fluid content and had become concentrated. What caused the fluid to escape from the vessels, and where did it go? No one knew.

These questions remained unanswered until the doctors, surgeons, and scientists returned to their laboratories. However, some transfusions were given, wherever possible, and in most cases they worked, supposedly by replacing the "lost" blood.

When the war was finally over, scientists centered their attack on the knotty problem that had proved so costly to human life. The shock process was obviously complicated, and many different approaches were necessary. Following up various hunches, some searched for a poison they thought was released from crushed tissues; others believed the adrenal gland somehow failed to produce enough of a chemical that kept the blood pressure normal; still others thought damage to the delicate walls of the capillaries permitted fluid to escape into the tissues. A few began to study the blood itself.

They found that by keeping blood from clotting with sodium citrate, and whirling it around in a centrifuge, the solids — mostly red and white blood cells — settled, and the plasma rose to the top of the centrifuge tube. Examination of the plasma showed that besides water it contained chiefly salts and proteins. In shock, the proteins, which by osmotic pressure normally attract water and keep it inside the vessels, escaped through the damaged walls. The blood therefore failed to hold onto its fluid volume, and became too thick to flow. In other words, the *hemoconcentration,* or blood thickening, in shock was due to leakage of the plasma. Perhaps instead of whole blood, plasma could be used, or just a salt solution, to restore the circulating volume.

This was tried in animals, in shock from extensive damage to their tissues. While the salt solution raised the blood pressure and maintained the flow, it was only a stopgap, soon leaking out. But plasma worked. It was the blood proteins, then, that were indispensable for holding the fluid inside the vessels. In shock, these large protein molecules escaped through the damaged capillary walls, drawing water with them into the tissue spaces.

The other symptoms followed logically: the lowered blood volume caused the pressure to drop, accounting for the thin, feeble pulse. The thickened blood made the flow sluggish and thus cut down the amount of oxygen supplied to the tissues. Hence the pallor and cold skin, the blue color in the transparent tissues over the lips.

After a decade or more of experimenting, plasma finally became standard in treating shock. It had several advantages over whole blood. Since it did not need to be matched by type, it could be given to anyone, and it could be stored in bottles for as long as two years. It was especially useful in emergencies such as fires, floods, and other major disasters.

A further improvement came in 1935, when an easy way was found to preserve and transport plasma. It was first frozen, in which form its keeping qualities were good, then dried into less bulky flakes by evaporation in a vacuum. Packed in tiny ampules, the plasma was shipped in a unit with a pint of sterile water and tubing. It needed only disolving in the water to be ready for injection.

In this form it was sent as "Plasma for Britain" in World War II, and to the Pacific after the attack on Pearl Harbor. By the middle of 1942, 325,000 blood donations had been collected. But this was only "a drop in the bucket" to what was coming. All over the United States and Canada, centers were set up by the Red Cross for the donation, collection, and processing of blood into plasma. Millions of the life-saving packets were shipped to the front lines and literally into every foxhole.

Of course plasma was not the complete solution. While it was useful in most cases of shock, it could not replace the blood loss from a severe hemorrhage. For this the patient needed whole blood with its oxygen-carrying red cells. And though there were always willing donors on the scene, they were not enough to supply the huge quantities necessary.

But in the meantime, before World War II, the Russians had discovered that citrated whole blood could be stored for many months at refrigerator temperatures without deterioration. The Blood Bank, with blood already typed and labeled, now came into existence. The first large-scale Blood Bank was organized in 1936 by Dr. Norman Bethune, the Canadian doc-

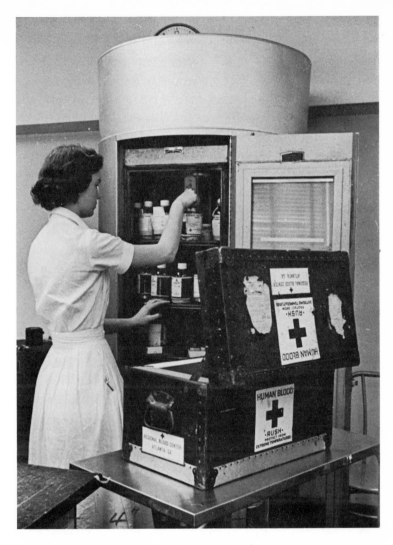

A blood bank showing the ice chest in which donors' blood is stored by type

tor. The first use of blood from a Blood Bank, in the Spanish Civil War, showed that it could be transported with ease.

Later on blood was similarly banked in the United States. Over thirteen million pints were given by voluntary donors during the war years. About one-third of the population have type O blood; they are the *universal donors* whose blood can be given safely to people with any type. So type O blood was saved for whole blood transfusions, while the rest was turned into dried plasma. As a result, the mortality rate among the wounded was less than half that in World War. I.

Today there are Blood Banks in every large hospital. No longer is there any need to search at the last minute for a proper donor. Should a patient undergoing surgery require blood, a bottle with the right label is ready in the bank. To keep the bank full, a member of the patient's family usually gives a pint to replace the one used. It doesn't matter if it isn't the same type, just as long as the bank always has enough of each one.

The precise cause of shock is still not known. If a poisonous substance is indeed released, as is generally believed, its identity has not yet been discovered. But recognizing the earliest signs, surgeons can now restore the fluid balance between the blood and the tissues by promptly giving blood substitutes, salt solution, plasma, or transfusions.

And research goes on to find the cause of shock and newer and better methods to prevent it.

———

When Crile was grappling with the problem, he discovered that during shock neither the brain nor the heart tissues suffered any apparent deterioration. The heart continued beating, its faster-than-normal rhythm partly compensating for the low blood pressure, and since even in the last stages of shock patients often remained conscious, the brain must have been receiving enough oxygen.

One of the latest technical aids in surgery is based on the knowledge that these two vital organs are sufficiently rugged to withstand temporary oxygen deprivation. The technique, called *hypothermia* (sub-body temperature), simulates a short-lived "hibernation" or "suspended animation" in human tissues. When the cold of winter comes, the groundhog and bear go into the dormant state of hibernation, all the body processes slow down, and the tissues need very little oxygen to remain alive. When spring comes, the tissues warm up again and go into a higher level of activity requiring more oxygen.

This state of hypothermia is achieved in humans by immersing the body in ice water, chilling an organ by placing ice directly on it, or circulating cooled blood with the heart-lung machine. The heart is slowed down, the oxygen demand of the body is lowered, and a degree of anesthesia is produced.

Hypothermia is mainly a surgical aid. Either the entire body or only certain organs, such as the heart, brain, or kidney, may be cooled. For instance, by cooling the blood from the carotid artery which furnishes the principal blood supply to the brain, the temperature of the brain can be brought down to 65 degrees, while the rest of the body may be maintained at the safe level of about 80 degrees. In this way operations on the brain may be almost bloodless.

Another of the many uses of hypothermia is in the prevention of shock. The tissues, at their much-slowed-up level of activity, withstand oxygen deprivation without damage.

With this and the other techniques at his command, the modern surgeon no longer need fear the loss of patients, even the elderly ones, through shock.

CHAPTER SIXTEEN

Spare Parts for Mending

Almost hidden away on the tenth floor of a hospital in mid-
town New York, you will find a modest office and a small
laboratory. Here a strange kind of business is carried on, for
there is no exchange of either money or purchasable prod-
ucts. Yet the telephone switchboard is open 24 hours a day,
365 days a year! The sign on the door — EYE BANK FOR
SIGHT RESTORATION, Inc. — tells that its business is to
restore sight to those who would otherwise live in darkness.
If you happened to be visiting when a telephone message came
in (collect from anywhere in the United States), you would
find out how quickly and efficiently this office-laboratory
functions.

The call may be from the attending doctor, from a hospital, or from a relative of an eye donor who has just died.
The staff goes into immediate action. Arrangements are made
by telephone for a doctor in the area to remove the eyes, as
soon as possible — a few hours after death at the latest. Then
either a local eye-bank representative or the Red Cross packs
the eyes in a sterile refrigerated container and takes them to
the nearest airport, from where they are flown on the very

next plane to one of seventeen branches or to the main New York office. They are then rushed to the laboratory for examination.

If the eyes are found to be healthy and suitable for transplantation, a staff member consults the office area's waiting list of persons eligible to receive the precious legacy — a healthy cornea to replace one that is hopelessly diseased or injured. Because of the great demand, the two eligibles on the top of the list of registered applicants are considered, one for each of the available corneas. Their doctors are immediately called: "Can you bring your patient in for a transplant? Is it possible for you to arrange for a hospital admission and an operating room? Please call back within the hour, Doctor."

If arrangements cannot be made at this time for applicant A or B, the staff member contacts patient C, for time is of the essence: the donor's cornea must be used within four or five days — preferably within forty-eight hours.

In the United States today there are 30,000 people who are blind — in both eyes — because the normally transparent tissue over the eyeball no longer admits light into the eye. The cornea has become clouded through disease or has been scarred by accident. But sight can be restored with the transplanting of a healthy, clear cornea, as we would replace an old window pane with a new one.

The cornea is the only tissue in the body that is truly transferable from one person to another. That it could be transferred has been known for about half a century, but the Eye-Bank, the agency that collects, preserves, and redistributes salvaged eyes and corneal tissue for grafting, was not organized until 1944. The story of the development of the technique of this operation takes us back to the last century, when a few courageous doctors dared to grapple with the problem.

In the days when corneal transplantation was considered a "bold fantasy of surgery," attempts were made to replace a damaged cornea with transparent crystals or corneas from the eyes of rabbits and dogs. The non-living replacements did not work at all, and the animal corneas, even when the graft "took," became opaque as soon as the donor tissue's own nourishment was exhausted. In the 1870's Eugen Von Hippel, a German surgeon, invented a circular trephine to cut out the corneas, but he was frustrated in his efforts to obtain a permanent transplant from dog to man. Others also failed, and it became clear that animal tissues would not "take."

Sporadically, when an otherwise useless eye had to be removed, a surgeon would try to transplant a piece of the cornea to a blind person, and occasionally it worked. The first successful operation, in 1905, brought renewed vision to an Austrian day laborer, Alois Glogar, whose cornea had been destroyed by spurting caustic lime. An eleven-year-old boy was in the same hospital in Olmütz, one of his eyes permanently damaged by an iron splinter. Dr. Edward Zirm removed the eye and, using the Von Hippel trephine, cut from it a circular disc of tissue about the size of a dime and grafted it in the same sized space cut in Glogar's eye. The graft took, but a workable, reliable technique, one that could be counted on to succeed every time, was still lacking. One of the great early obstacles was the difficulty in finding two suitable patients at the same time: one whose eye had to be removed, and another whose eye needed grafting.

In 1955, Vladimir Petrovich Filatov celebrated his 80th birthday and the 43rd anniversary of his method of corneal grafting. The son of a surgeon and oculist, Filatov was born in 1875 in the village of Mikhailov, about sixty miles southeast of Moscow. While a student, he spent his vacations as a helper in his father's dispensary. The many hopelessly blind people he saw there convinced him that combatting blindness was the most noble of undertakings, and he was determined to become an oculist and devote his studies to the restoration of sight.

After graduation from Moscow University in 1897, he began his work as a physician in a Moscow eye hospital. Busy as he was with his patients, he never forgot his resolve to restore vision to those whose eyes were normal but for the opaque window panes. For the next fifteen years, most of them spent at the Odessa Eye Clinic, Filatov experimented with and finally, in 1912, perfected the technique of transplantation. He overcame many of the difficulties and complications: damage to the lens, support for the transplant, and various other inadequacies of previous operations. "It was a thorny path which could be cleared only by great efforts and thought," he wrote in his memoirs.

He then went on to solve the other half of the problem — how to get corneas to transplant — and showed that tissue obtained from a fresh cadaver was just as satisfactory as that from a living person. Removed within a few hours after death, the eyes could be subjected to laboratory tests to select the tissue with the most promising healing powers, and this could be kept for two or three days in a refrigerated, sterile receptacle. Thus the idea of an Eye Bank became a practicality.

Since the Eye Bank in the United States was established, over five thousand have had their sight restored. Says Dr. R. Townley Paton, its founder, Vice President, and Medical Director: "Eventual success in dealing with this major cause of blindness will be one of the greatest contributions to eye welfare."

Corneal grafting is performed by an eye surgeon. This specialty is but an offshoot and one small branch of the parent art of transplantation of tissue.

Strange as it seems, plastic surgery is at least as old as surgery itself, and has nothing to do with modern plastics, the word having come from the Greek, meaning to mold. Mutilated ear lobes and noses were mended by the Hindu surgeons of ancient India, the operation developing out of dire necessity because these amputations were meted out as legal punishment for many crimes and perpetrated as private revenge.

The oldest method of transplanting skin, still called the Indian method, consisted of lifting and *rotating* a flap from the forehead so that it could be implanted where needed. When the graft had taken, the flap was severed from the forehead and the ends shaped into a new nose. The operation was performed by the caste of potters, who kept the art secret by handing it down only from father to son, in the manner of the Asklepiads.

Although mentioned by Celsus, Galen, and Paul of Aegina, the art seems to have been lost or ignored by European surgeons until the sixteenth century, when skin grafting began independently in France and Italy. In the French or *sliding flap* method, the skin was not rotated; instead, the free tissue was made to slide or advance to cover an adjacent site. The Italian or *distant flap* method, still largely used today, was developed, though not invented, by Gaspare Tagliacozzi of Bologna.

"We bring back, refashion and restore to wholesomeness the features which nature gave but chance destroyed, not that they may charm the eye but that they may be an advantage to the living soul, not as a mean artifice but as an alleviation of illness, not as becomes charlatans but as becomes good physicians and followers of the great Hippocrates. For although the original beauty of the face is indeed restored, yet this is only accidental, and the end for which the physician is working is that the features should fulfill their offices according to nature's decree . . . "

In that era of duels, family feuds, constant wars, and cold steel, the loss of nose, ears, and lips was common, and men of high station would endure almost any pain to have their faces restored. Others were mutilated by accident or disease, and long before the days of asepsis and anesthetics, Tagliacozzi was surprisingly successful in replacing lost parts of the face. Unlike his immediate predecessors, the Sicilian surgeon Branca and his son, he refused to operate in secret, teaching his method to many pupils and writing that he rejoiced "to offer it to the use of all mankind . . . For I am not such as to wish that this art should remain with me in shackles . . . but desire that it should go far and wide, even among other peoples. For this reason, too, I have given everyone the opportunity of watching while I operated." In the same spirit he published his *De Curtorum chirurgia per Insitionem*, giving full instructions on how to use the method and providing some twenty illustrations, drawn by himself.

By the technique he perfected, Tagliacozzi separated a measured flap of skin from the upper arm and sutured the free end to the nose. He kept the arm motionless by binding it to the head with a series of bandages. When after three weeks the graft "took" (the skin flap united with the nose tissues), he cut the skin at the base of the flap, released the arm, and shaped the grafted skin into a new or mended nose.

For a number of years his pupils carried on Tagliacozzi's work, but apparently they did not have either his surgical or teaching skill, because for the next two and a half centuries plastic surgery fell into general disuse. Perhaps one of the reasons was the two-fold difficulty that plagued all types of surgery — pain and infection — and in less capable hands than Tagliacozzi's, the operation was practically abandoned.

Then in 1840, in Boston, it was reported that Dr. Jonathan Mason Warren was using *free* grafts. For the first time, small, entirely detached pieces of skin were taken from the arm or thigh to fill in gaps in the wound to be mended. Soon other surgeons in France and Germany tried to transplant larger sections of free skin. Carl Thiersch, in 1886, described to the German Surgical Association the successful grafting of *wide ribbons* of skin, by using not only the upper (epidermal) layer but also the underlying dermis, which contains the blood vessels. Two things were thus accomplished: larger pieces could be transplanted, and healing was more likely to occur. Today, almost any thickness of skin may be cut with an electric razor machine, to suit each need.

Halsted later improved the procedure by his aseptic technique, making it unnecessary to change the dressing for at least a week after suturing, and thus promoting still faster healing under sterile conditions.

Modern reconstructive surgery gained further impetus during World War I when Filatov, by this time an experienced plastic surgeon, introduced a fourth transplant method — the tube pedicle — which increased the possibilities of success when skin was taken away from an area quite far from the defect. The idea occurred to him in the course of planning an operation on a young soldier whose face had been so grossly scarred that distant areas would have to be used to obtain enough skin to fully cover the mutilations.

Filatov made two parallel slits in the skin, held up the skin with a "skin hook," undermined it with a knife, and joined

Vladimir P. Filatov

the ends of the flap freed on the two long sides, by suturing the tissue into a closed tube. The underlying slits were also sutured, closing off the donor area. The tube pedicle was like a handle on a closed suitcase. This procedure insured normal nutrition in the flap which retained the circulation, and was a deterrent to infection. Some time later he detached the tube at one end and transplanted it to the part of the body to be mended. By "migrating caterpillar" fashion, as each transplantation took, the other end was cut and transplanted forward. The use of the tube pedicle assumed its greatest significance during World War II in the repair of many types of serious battle wounds.

Today plastic surgery is used to heal extensive burns, wounds, laceration, and frostbite, to correct deformities from any cause, to mend fractured jaws and noses, to repair joints and even internal organs. There is almost no structural abnormality of any part of the body that the skillful plastic surgeon cannot "mold" and restore to wholesomeness and use-fulness, according to the aims and standards set down by Tagliacozzi nearly four centuries ago.

At the time of this writing, a brand new kind of surgery is just coming over the horizon: the correction of abnormal-ities of birth. Of course most babies are and always have been born without serious structural defects. But who can count the number of those born with these defects who since time immemorial have died shortly after birth? Now these new-borns can be saved by surgery. Frequently they must be operated on within the first three days of life, for the condi-tions crucial to infant survival demand instant treatment.

While the fetus is developing, so many things can go wrong and produce defects in the child! The esophagus may end in a blind pouch, or its lower end communicate with the trachea instead of the stomach; the stomach may be obstructed or the intestine strangulated; part of the intestine may pro-trude into the umbilical cord; a hernia in the diaphragm may push the intestine up into the chest; the anus may be closed. Any number of things can go wrong with the heart and blood vessels: there may be a narrowing of the aorta, a hole in the wall separating the chambers of the heart, or a *patent ductus arteriosus*, as in the case of Mabel Chin.

The surgeon can wait safely for several years before cor-recting some of the defects: cleft palate, water on the brain, premature closure of skull sutures, certain heart abnormalities. But other conditions, which interfere with breathing or feed-ing, need immediate surgery if the baby is to survive.

In this highly specialized field, every operation taxes to the utmost the ingenuity and skill of even the virtuoso surgeon. According to one specialist, pediatric surgery, compared with other types, is like repairing a tiny Swiss watch instead of a grandfather clock. And full knowledge of shock, hemorrhage control, suture materials, prevention of infection, and the precise replacement of fluids is essential.

Corneal transplantation has been solved by the Eye Bank. The prevention of hemorrhage and shock has been indispensably aided by the Blood Bank. The latest life-saving institution is the Tissue Bank.

The cornea, the only tissue truly transplantable from one person to another, is unique: skin is graftable only in the same person, from one part of the body to another. A razor-thin section of skin is taken from the belly, chest, or thigh — the *donor* area — to patch a hand or chin — the *recipient* area. This is called an *autograft*. Except in the case of identical twins, grafts from another person, called *homografts*, do not "take." But they have their uses.

When a person is severely burned and weakened, and large areas have to be resurfaced *without delay*, a homograft is necessary. As "biologic dressings," homografts are often life saving in such patients. The wound is not only temporarily closed by the graft that lasts about three weeks, but it is also protected against drying and the loss of precious tissue fluids, proteins, and salts. A homograft also provides a respite from pain, diminishes the risk of infection, acts as a barrier to mechanical damage, stimulates healing, and, until it disappears, tides the patient over until a smaller *autograft* can be applied.

No single donor can supply the required tissue for a badly burned patient without danger to himself: as many as thirty donors have been needed to furnish enough for one such patient. Obviously this is not practical, for each donor requires hospitalization and wound care. Here's where the Tissue Banks come in.

Among the first to be set up was the one at National Naval Medical Center in Bethesda, Maryland. Here life-saving "spare parts," formerly thrown away — skin, bone, cartilage, fascia — are now saved and stored by "freeze-dying." Under these conditions even tissue taken after death, or bone from amputated limbs — if it is taken immediately — can be used. Removed aseptically, folded in saline antiseptic gauze, and stored in sterile containers, it is there when needed. Kept at a temperature of 3 to 5 degrees Centigrade, the tissue retains its "graftability" for weeks.

Many of the larger hospitals where plastic surgery is performed now have banks that stock tissue for body repairs. In a plea for the creation of these skin banks, a French surgeon has called the practice of using living donors "barbarous," contrasting it with the noble and satisfying gift of a person who bequeaths his skin to save the life of another.

One of the uncrossed frontiers of plastic surgery is the casting off of the homograft by the recipient's tissues, as it would reject any foreign body or substance. This problem is now under intensive study. When this frontier is crossed, an exciting new aspect of restorative surgery will be opened. And the cell biologists, biochemists, immunologists, and surgeons who are working on the problem look forward confidently to a time when Tissue Banks will dispense sections of blood vessels, nerves, and even whole organs for permanent transplantation.

We have seen in the long story of surgery how many operations, once considered impossible, have been made both safe and restorative. So in the future will man's limitless ingenuity bring about still undreamed-of discoveries and creations in the art and science of tissue regeneration.

ACKNOWLEDGMENTS

In recounting the story of science, a new book is but an extension of the work of others: the giants who made and continue to make science history, and the chroniclers who, since ancient times, have told it. The value of the new lies in making these more readily available to the emerging makers of science and future masters of the scalpel among the young readers of today. The author is keenly aware of her indebtedness to the many rich sources upon which she drew and to all those who in varied ways have given generously of their help.

This brief acknowledgment is but a token of thanks to Dr. Richard C. Reed, surgeon, The Babies' Hospital-Coit Memorial, Newark, N.J., for his critical reading of the manuscript, and his courtesy in making possible visits to the operating rooms of which he has charge; to Dr. Jerome Gelb for his valuable correction of Chapter 16, and for the privilege of observing him operate with a master hand; to Dr. Paul Muller, Harlem Eye and Ear Hospital, for a similar courtesy, making possible the opportunity to see delicate operations to restore vision; to Mr. Al Friedman of the New York Heart Association for the showing of the film on the Mabel Chin heart operation, and to Dr. Jere W. Lord, Jr. for reading the chapter that tells about it; to Mrs. Cornelius P. Rhoads and her staff who provided an inspiring visit to the Eye Bank; to Dr. R. Townley Paton for checking the section dealing with its sight-restoring work.

The author also wishes to thank most gratefully all those who have given permission to reproduce the photographs:

Mr. William R. Breyer, Office of Public Information, The American National Red Cross, for the pictures on pages 11, 284, and 299; "Journal of the International College of Surgeons," for the pictures on pages 18, 19, and 20, from Vol. 28, October, 1957, and for the picture on page 25 from Vol.

32, July, 1959. The pictures on pages 114 and 119 are reprinted by kind permission of the President and Council of the Royal College of Surgeons of England; Macmillan & Co. Ltd., London for the pictures on pages 154, 159, 166, 171, 188, and 205, all from *Lord Lister* by Sir Rickman Godlee; Section of Publications, Mayo Clinic, for the pictures on pages 178, 204, 207, and 215; Paul D. MacLean, M.D., executor of John F. Fulton Collection, for pictures on pages 239, 246, 262, and 263 from Fulton, John F., *Harvey Cushing, A Biography*, 1946. Courtesy of Charles C. Thomas, Publisher, Springfield, Illinois; pictures on pages 180, 192, 202, and 211 from *The Doctors Mayo* by Helen Clapesattle, by permission of the publishers, University of Minnesota Press, Minneapolis. All pictures not mentioned above are from the Photo Collection of the New York Academy of Medicine, New York.

Many of the numerous sources for this book are not easily accessible to the young reader — out-of-print books, scientific journals, and works in foreign languages — but among those easily available, these will offer exciting additional reading: *The New Science of Surgery*, 1946, by Frank G. Slaughter, Messner; *The Century of the Surgeon*, 1957, and *Triumph of Surgery*, 1960, by Thorwald Jurgen, Pantheon Press; *Henry E. Sigerist, on the History of Medicine*, edited by Félix Marti-Ibanez, MD Publications, 1960; *Devils, Drugs and Doctors* by Howard W. Haggard, Harper & Brothers, 1929; *Victory Over Pain*, by Victor Robinson, Henry Schuman, 1946; *Scalpel*, by Agatha Young, Random House, 1956; *The Doctors Mayo*, by Helen Clapesattle, University of Minnesota Press, 2nd edition, 1960; *The Reluctant Surgeon* by John Kobler, Doubleday, 1960; *The Surgeon's Tale* by Robert G. Richardson, Scribner's, 1958; *Men with Golden Hands* by Emil Hanze Georg Lutz, Appleton, 1956.

INDEX

Pember Library and Museum
Granville, New York
HOURS

2 P. M.-6 P. M. daily.
7 P. M. - 9 P. M. Monday, Wednesday, Friday.

The library is free to all residents of the Village and Town of Granville. Non-residents may secure full library privileges by payment of the established non-resident fee.

All books except popular new fiction may be kept two weeks and may be renewed.

New books of fiction may be kept one week and may not be renewed.

Current periodicals may be kept one week.

Borrowers are responsible for the loss of, and damage to, books and periodicals charged to them.

Five cents a day is charged for each seven day book kept overtime. Two cents a day is charged for all others.